MY WITNESSES

My Witnesses

(An "Uncommentary" on the Book of Acts)

By Mark E. Moore

ISBN 0-89900-249-8

To order copies of this book contact Mark Moore:

markmoore@occ.edu

Or send $12.50 to

Mark E. Moore
Ozark Christian College
1111 N. Main
Joplin, MO 64801

Dedicated to:

Mark Scott

First my teacher,
then my yoke-fellow,
always my brother.

Author's Introduction

In the summer of 1999 I found myself on an archaeological expedition in Macedonia. Feeling obligated to bring my wife some sort of souvenir, I stumbled into a kiosk that specialized in cheap pottery. The aggressive, leathery-skinned clerk was zealous about his wares. Recognizing that he was dealing with an experienced traveler and discerning scholar, he bypassed the trinkets on the street and took me into the interior of the shop where he proudly disclosed his "private collection." I'm not quite sure what kind of wave of romantic gullibility overcame me at that moment, but there was one particular pot I was drawn to. It had an almost magical spell over my mind. It was an oblong vase approximately 15 inches in length and 12 inches in diameter. It was sealed on both ends and laid on its side like a giant "wilted" egg. Honestly, it was not particularly beautiful, but it had mystique. So I paid what I thought at the time was far too much for a plain piece that my sultry friend assured me was an ancient pot. I packed it tightly with my dirty laundry inside a sturdy cardboard box and positioned it strategically at the very center of my duffle bag.

When I returned home I opened my bag with my wife and kids around me. They were bubbling with anticipation to see the ancient treasures I had acquired for them. When I opened the box, however, I was crestfallen. Some brute baggage handler had crushed the box and cracked my prized pot. Surveying the damage, I decided that some SuperGlue and TLC could salvage the treasure. My daughter, Megan, and I spread out the pot on the kitchen table and went to work. There were three main breaks that needed repair. I was using her little fingers to gently hold it all together. Suddenly one of the pieces gave way and slipped inside the pot. As she reached in, ever so gently, to retrieve it, she discovered that there was something else in the pot. We raced for a flashlight, and to our amazement, we discovered that it was a roll of papyri inside. At the risk of ruining the pot, we gently chipped away the cracked end of the pot and extracted no less than 52 single sheets of papyri. Each one of them was inscribed with uncial Greek letters. I understood well what this must mean. It was more than my heart could take! The shop-keeper had told the truth. The contents of the pot proved it to be at least fifteen hundred years old.

Immediately I phoned two of my colleagues. One was a master of ancient Greek, the other a renowned archaeologist. The three of us stood dumbfounded at what we held in our hands. Little did we know just how significant this find was, however. Our expert archaeologist called a friend of his who was head of the antiquities department at a major Texas university (which for legal purposes must remain nameless). When we told him about the find, he insisted that we transport it to his lab for analysis. This was, of course, precisely what we had hoped to hear. That weekend we packed our bags and flew south.

Our Texas friend had assembled a team of five paleo-linguists. Two of them went to work analyzing the pot with our own archaeologist, three of them (along with myself and our Greek guru), set out translating the 52 Greek letters. As the uncial Greek took shape in English, we soon realized that this was a very old collection of letters pertaining to early Christianity. Someone had deliberately collected these documents and sealed them in the pot for safe-keeping. After three hours, we had translated some fourteen letters. Individually, we were all coming to the same shocking conclusion. Conferring with one another only confirmed our hypothesis. At about this same time, those working on the pot bolted from the lab. They agreed with our own archaeologist. "This pot," they declared, "almost certainly comes from the first century, and likely from the mid to late sixties!" Our conclusion from the linguistic side was no less significant. We held in our hands what appeared to be original accounts of the beginnings of the Christian movement as recorded in the New Testament book of Acts! This inspired the whole team to work on completing the translations. We were too excited to eat or sleep. By the end of the weekend we had completed our rough translation of all 52 letters.

We were nearly certain that what we had acquired was the equivalent of Doctor Luke's file-folder of original eye-witness testimony upon which he based his second volume – Acts. We each made copies of the translations of the others. We decided, for security purposes, to leave the printed documents in Texas. I did, however, email the electronic file to my office in Joplin, MO.

Coming home we were delayed out of Dallas due to inclement weather. When we arrived in Tulsa International, still dizzy from our find, we saw on the news that the storm we just left had struck the very university which housed our treasure. Unbelievably, an electrical storm had short-circuited the computers in the lab and started a fire that decimated the entire floor of the antiquities department. After several frantic phone calls, we received the worst news we could have heard. All was lost, the pot, the papyri, the original translations. The only remaining trace of this work was the single email copy of our cursory translations. I was able to retrieve this file and I humbly offer it to you, my dear reader, in the following manuscript.

Mark E. Moore

May 16, 2000

P.S. I realize that this may be difficult to believe and I wouldn't much blame you if you didn't. In fact, the preceding tale is based purely on a figment of my own imagination for rhetorical purposes and bears no resemblance to reality.

Table of Contents

Text:		Title:	Page:
1.	1:1-11	A Letter from Theophilus	2
2.	1:12-26	A Letter from Matthias	5
3.	2:1-13	An Excerpt from Matthew's Diary	9
4.	2:14-47	A Letter from Andronicus (Rom 16:7)	12
5.	3:1-26	A Testimony from Hallomenos	15
6.	4:1-22	A Press Release from Alexander	19
7.	4:23-37	A Letter from Joseph	22
8.	5:1-16	An Interview with Nicanor	25
9.	5:17-42	A Memo from Gamaliel to Saul	29
10.	6:1-15	A Letter to a Skeptic	32
11.	7:1-60	A Letter to an Ex-skeptic	35
12.	8:1-25	A Letter from Philip	38
13.	8:26-40	A Travel Report from Tumbasi	41
14.	9:1-31	A Memo from Jonathan	45
15.	9:32-43	A Newspaper Clipping Concerning Aeneas & Dorcas	48
16.	10:1-8, 24-48	A Letter from Cornelius	51
17.	10:9-23	An Investigative Report	55
18.	11:19-30	A Letter from Lucius	59
19.	12:1-19	A Psalm by Mary in Celebration of Peter's Release	62
20.	12:20-25	An Historical Annotation from Josephus' Antiquities XIX.8.2	64
21.	13:1-3	Board Meeting Minutes	66
22.	13:4-12	A Memo from Sergius Paulus	69
23.	13:13-52	An Interview with Paul	71
24.	14:1-20	A Letter from Eunice	76
25.	14:21-28	A Letter from Gaius of Derbe	79
26.	15:1-21	A Letter from Titus	81
27.	15:22-35	An Open Letter from James and Judas	84
28.	15:36-41	An Excerpt from John Mark's Diary	86
29.	16:1-10	Journal Entry #1	88

30. 16:11-40   A History of the 1ˢᵗ Christian Church of
               Philippi, by Lydia and Zōn 90
31. 17:1-9   A Letter from Jason:
               An Update on Paul, #1 96
32. 17:10-15   A Letter from Timothy:
               An Update on Paul, #2 98
33. 17:16-34   A Testimony by Dionysius 100
34. 18:1-17   A Letter from Sosthenes:
               An Update on Paul, #3 104
35. 18:18-28   A Letter from Priscilla to Paul 107
36. 19:1-10   A Letter from Apollos to Tyrannus . . . 109
37. 19:11-20   A Newspaper Clipping: Seven Streakers
               Lead to Book Burning 111
38. 19:21-41   A Report by Protagoras,
               City Clerk of Ephesus 113
39. 20:1-21:16 A Travel Log from Aristarchus 116
40. 20:7-12   A Letter from Eutychus 119
41. 20:17-35   A Sermon Critique by Tychicus 121
42. 21:17-36   An Open Letter from James,
               to the Church of Judea 124
43. 21:37-22:29 A Roman Guard's Request for
               Information about the Way 127
44. 22:30-23:11 A Secret Memo from Nicodemus 131
45. 23:12-30   A Secret Memo from Joseph
               of Arimathea 134
46. 23:31-24:26 A Report by Philip's oldest daughter,
               via Cornelius' wife 136
47. 25:1-12   Trial Record #251-12, by Philologus . . 140
48. 25:13-26:32 Correspondence from Manaen 142
49. 27:1-44   A Travel Report by Julius 146
50. 28:1-10   A Letter from Publius 150
51. 28:11-28   A Report by Aquila 152
52. 28:30-31   Prologue by Luke 154

December 5, A.D. 62

Dr. Luke
Apt. 238
412 Coliseum St.
Rome, Italy

Dr. Luke,

It was with great joy and satisfaction I received the final draft of volume two this morning. You will be relieved to know that it arrived by courier without incident. Rest assured, I believe in this project more strongly than ever. I fully intend to fund its reproduction and distribution. Not only will I publish your set, I intend to promote it among the other Equestrian noblemen. A number of them have already read your first work on Jesus' life. They were intrigued with this new story form you called "gospel," and they are keenly interested in the continuing saga of the Jesus movement in our own day.

I devoured this second work the very hour I opened the scroll. Such detail! Such drama! Indeed, others have written fine Greek plays, tragedies, or even epic biographies. But this, my friend, is a piece that will stand the test of time. While their works are appropriately named after their heroes — Acts of Thucydides, Acts of Thecla, etc. — ours must be named after our hero: The Acts of the **Holy Spirit**. Indeed, our Lord did not leave us alone, but as he ascended, his envoy descended to carry out the continuing work of the incarnation.

My mind is just racing! There are so many things about this work that are noteworthy. I know I can't address them all. Yet at the risk of honoring the author above the Author, I must enumerate a few of the more delightful and dynamic features. First, the way you bracketed the book with the "kingdom of God" (1:3 & 28:31), is a stroke of genius. That **is** the point after all. It is not about miracles, as wondrous as they are; nor about the pillars, Peter and Paul, as important as they are; nor even is it about the church and its development. In and of itself, the church is merely a mirage of the eternal kingdom of God. We are not subject to preachers or priests but a King; we don't have affiliation to members but kinship to citizens; we don't own property, we have dominion. Praise be to our God and Father who made us a kingdom of priests and princes!

Second, I was intrigued with how the two books were woven together. You phased out the first volume with the resurrection, giving but a glimpse of the ascension. I wanted more. To my delight I got it in volume two! With a brief review of the 40 days, you ushered in the ultimate raising of Jesus. What a scene! In one brief portrait you made plain the theology we had read about in Paul's letter to the Romans (8:34). This Son of Man was lifted on the clouds and became our intercessor with the Ancient of Days himself.

Third, I found in verse eight an outline for the book. I don't know if that was intentional or not, but I do know that it is significant. In ever widening circles the gospel emanates with power. Up to our own day it has been scandalized and brutalized, maligned and rejected. Yet it grows. As the Master said, this yeast permeates the entire world. Like dandelions kicked by a malicious child, the church has been abused by the Enemy's envoys. Yet the harder it's beaten the farther it's flung. I was struck by this story. Even when the church tried to recoil, even when it tried to go its own way, God's sovereign plan rolled on relentlessly. This is not the story of the brave and clever church. It is the story of God's immutable plan carried out by his immortal Spirit.

Let me close with this observation: Your document should prove valuable to your companion Paul in his upcoming trial before Nero. You have clearly articulated what we have found so true, Christianity is not a threat to the Empire but its salvation. Believers have demonstrated their love for humanity, their compassion for the poor, and their penchant for obedience and justice. Furthermore, at no time and at no place has the Way been dishonored in just judicial proceedings. We are better citizens for our fierce allegiance to our King. You have written a credible work with keen intellect and masterful literary style. You have clearly done your homework on politics, culture, geography, law and even sea travel (which delighted and surprised even me!). Yet you have bathed this intellectual feast in a simple faith of the risen Christ. Indeed God has visited our time and space. Your first book convinced me beyond any shadow of a doubt that Jesus is the Christ of God, but this second work has cut even closer to home. It has convinced me that I have a role to play in this continuing saga of God's eternal kingdom. Should there be a volume three, I pray that by God's grace I may contribute a verse.

For the Love of God,

Theophilus

P.S. Luke, I must tell you that your intellectual and historical presentation of Jesus is compelling. But more than these facts, your own life has won me over to Christianity. I remember you before you were a disciple. You were every bit as brilliant and such a fine physician! The problem was that you knew it all too well. You were so proud of your intellectual prowess, and your career was opportunistic, merely a means of self-promotion. But now that you have given your life to Christ, your writing radiates with compassion on the least and the lost. You have become a champion of children and women, the poor, the widow, the unclean, and even us "Gentiles." Your own life is a monument, reminding me that our transformation in Christ is real.

My Witnesses

Brother Luke,

I'm flattered by your interest in my story. But believe me, there is not much to tell. You yourself know what an insignificant role I played in the foundation of the church. Nonetheless, while I was never a major player, I was always more than a casual observer. I was there the day Jesus was baptized. I saw the Holy Spirit come down on him in bodily form as a dove, just as it did on us three years later in the form of fire. I too walked with Jesus through the trails of Galilee and the streets of Jerusalem. I was never included in the inner band, but then again, I was never far away. I was in the temple when he taught, on the shore when he calmed the storm, in the crowds when he raised the dead, and in the shadow of Golgotha when he died. I was even among the chosen who saw Him raised from the dead. I testify to you and all who will listen that I saw the nail prints with my own two eyes, and I was there that day on the Mount of Olives. Now there's a story you need to tell!

It was midmorning and the discussions about the kingdom were ringing the walls of the upper room in Mary's home. "When will you proclaim yourself king, Jesus?" "What is your political agenda for Israel?" "What will you do with the Romans?" About the only question that was *not* asked was, "Who will sit on your right and left?" There was so much we wanted to know. But all Jesus wanted to talk about was the mystery of the Spirit's coming and our obligation to take this gospel to all the world. Needless to say, we were mystified. What, pray tell, were we to preach? There were no specific details.

As if to clear the air, we took a walk. It was no secret where he was headed. We had been there before . . . lots. But the eleven walked tentatively up Olivet's slope. The ghosts of Gethsemane were still haunting. At the top of the hill, Jesus continued to talk about his kingdom. As usual, we were captivated. I can't really remember how long he preached. At first none of us noticed, we were so enraptured with His words. But then it was too obvious to miss. He was a good three feet off the ground! He continued to talk as he drifted toward heaven. We were dumbstruck, but Jesus gave no indication that He was the least bit amazed. He lectured on as if he were in Peter's boat, drifting out to the deep of Tiberias. We continued to stare in consternation, like children who lose a toy ship as it drifts down stream. Even when He was out of sight we stared at the sky trying to catch just one last glimpse.

We never noticed the messengers in white until they spoke. Their voices wrenched us back to reality, "Why are you staring at the sky? Just as surely as Jesus is gone, he will be back!" What were we to do? Wait. The upper room seemed like a better place than the top of Mt. Olives. So we made the trek back to Jerusalem, a little better than half a mile. There in the upper room was an auspicious group: The Eleven, Jesus' family (yes, even his half-brothers!), and a number of others. I would estimate there were around 120 of us. The moment seemed too solemn to speak, that is, at least to each other. So we began to pray, asking the Father the same things we had asked his Son just hours before. "What do we do now?" was really the gist of it. We felt a sense of awe from what God had done, but a sense of insecurity at our own inability. We didn't know what the next move was. We were eager to move, yet paralyzed. That's a frustration I cannot describe. So we continued to pray: "What now? What next?"

The answer came several days later through the mouth of Peter (we leaned heavily on him in these early days). When he stood to speak we were poised to listen. Of all the things he could have talked about, this is what we least wanted to hear: Judas. That traitor! That scallywag! That petty, money-grubbing weasel! He sold out the Author of Life for the price of a slave. He got what he deserved! The knot he tied with his own hands gave way under the tremors of God's earthquakes in Jerusalem. His bloated body fell down the steeps of the Potter's Field and speckled the cliffs with his bloody entrails. We spoke of him with disdain. But what went unsaid, I suspect, was what most of us were really thinking about. You see, we envied Judas when he carried the purse. And when Jesus set him in the most honored position during the last supper, we turned green. What bothered us most, I think, is that we all wanted to be like him and now realized we weren't that far off.

Nonetheless, as Peter pointed out through the Psalms (69:26): "Let his habitation be deserted and let another man stand in his stead." The fisherman even put it to a vote. "Who will it be?" he asked. Several names surfaced. They finally landed on two: Joseph Barsabbas (AKA Justus), and me. I couldn't believe my ears! It happened so fast I had no chance to consider the magnitude of what was taking place. Good thing too; I likely would have died on the spot. All those years I had skirted the edges of the inner circle. All those years I had grumbled to myself that I was more worthy than some of those Jesus had chosen. Now that my dreams were becoming reality I realized that Jesus was right all along not to choose me. Indeed I had followed him faithfully. Indeed, I pursued Him relentlessly. But none of these brothers knew my heart like I did. I was not worthy to sit on one of the twelve thrones. Oh, I had judged the tribes of Israel countless times. Unfortunately, it was all wrong-headed and wrong-hearted.

How good and right it was that they allowed Jesus to make the final decision through lots. Had they not, who would have accepted the congregation's vote? To be honest, I would have been the first to accept it and the first to doubt it. I know it seems strange to pick church leaders by lots, nor would I suggest it as a normal practice. But at that time, at that place, it was God-ordained. They put two stones in a basin. The black one was mine. They prayed. Peter lifted the bowl up to heaven as if it were an offering to God. Then he began to shake the bowl, gently at first. Several times both stones saluted the crowd as they peeked over the rim. Then, as if it were in slow motion, I saw the black stone rise high above the rim, seemingly plucked by an invisible hand. It fell to the floor. Silence fell with it. We stared at the stone with reverence almost like we had stared at the sky earlier. As the wonder of the moment lifted, we looked around at each other and continued to ask with our eyes, "What's next? What do we do now?" Not knowing what else to do, we prayed as never before. It would be nearly a week before Jesus would answer our question again.

Matthias

My Witnesses

May 18, A.D. 33

What a day! Where to begin? We had been hunkered down in the upper room for the past 10 days, not out of fear, but ignorance and obedience. Our natural impulse was to return to Galilee from whence we hailed. But Jesus had directed us to wait in the capital city until we were baptized with the Holy Spirit. We had no earthly idea what he meant, of course, nor did we know where to go. So we just sat tight and waited . . . but not passively. We prayed fervently, day after day.

Today began our Jewish celebration of Pentecost which marked the fifty day anniversary of the death of our Lord at Passover. This celebration commemorates the giving of the law to Moses on Mt. Sinai. But today, we were given a greater gift by far. As usual, this feast attracted even larger crowds than Tabernacles or Passover. People from distant lands swarmed the streets while we remained in the upper room and prayed. This morning we, the Twelve, including our most recent addition, Matthias, prayed with particular vigor and anticipation. We were not to be disappointed.

As we sought the Lord, He came to us just as he had promised. We began to hear the rumblings of a storm. It grabbed our attention since this is the dry season in Jerusalem. The sound of a wind (not wind itself, mind you, but merely its sound) rushed through the room. It reminded me of the time we were with Jesus in a boat on Tiberias when he calmed the storm. Yet this time he caused it. To be sure, we were now praying with our eyes wide open. And what we saw! It was like a sheet of fire. Only instead of the flames flickering upward to the sky, they divided downward above each of our heads! In a flash of inspiration, we knew as if we had one mind, that this moment must not be kept private. We migrated from Mary's house to the temple courts. It is only about a ten minute walk. We got there about an hour before brunch.

The crowds were flabbergasted, as were we. They gathered around each of us while we explained to them the gospel of salvation. I began to notice that all of the men before me were

Parthian proselytes. Then it struck me. I was no longer speaking in Aramaic, I was speaking in the dialect of these men. You must understand, I never studied Parthian in my life! Their attentiveness was not due to my oratory skill. They were dumbstruck by a hillbilly from Galilee who spoke fluent Parthian. Who can blame them? I was too! I began to survey my comrades. They too had each collected a crowd of like descent. There were at least fifteen distinct people groups we spoke to that day. The tower of Babel took a beating as the distinctions of language disappeared.

"What is that sound? What will become of all this?" they asked. It was a perfect platform for Peter's first sermon, which I have entitled: "The Sound of Salvation." To be sure, some were skeptics. Of all things, they accused us of being drunk so early in the day! Peter appropriately pointed out how ludicrous their accusation was. Then we watched as Peter pulled out the keys of the Kingdom and unlocked the gates of God. What we had wondered about for the past ten days (really for the past three years), suddenly made sense. Without human explanation, we now understood that Jesus was establishing the kingdom of *heaven.*

Peter's use of the Bible was brilliant. You must pardon my penchant for fulfilled prophecy, but never was it so appropriate. From the prophet Joel (2:28-32), he showed how this moment was inscribed in the annals of eternity. The descent of the Holy Spirit changed everything! He opened up the revelation of God to young and old alike, to both male and female. And I thought the veil in the temple was torn in two before! Now for sure, there is nothing separating us from our glorious God! Indeed Joel spoke truth: In these Last Days there would be miracles in heaven and on earth. With our own eyes we have seen the lame walk, the dumb speak, demons cast out and the dead raised. Many of these miracles were performed by our own hands. But the greatest of all miracles awaited this day, this magnificent moment in human history, when "all who call on the name of the Lord shall be saved." And they did! Three thousand strong! This ex-tax collector had a heyday counting that roll call.

My Witnesses

Peter proved with Psalm 16 that David was not the eternal king of Israel, rather it was Jesus. He was buried for three days but escaped corruption by being raised from the dead! We have seen it with our own eyes and testify. This rumor of grave robbers was ridiculous and the crowds knew it. The rumor of an empty tomb was true and they knew that as well. Even if they didn't, a ten minute stroll would settle the question.

What, then, do we conclude of this Jesus? As Peter pointed out, again from the Psalms (110), he is the risen Christ now seated at the right hand of God ready to use his enemies as his footstool. Just then it struck us all, the crowd and the Twelve alike. Here we were, a bunch of backwoodsmen, accusing the religious elite of the murder of the Messiah. The silence was thick, the pause was pregnant. Then Peter put a thunderous exclamation point on the sermon when he said, "Be it known to all Israel, this Jesus you lifted up on a cross, God exalted as Lord and Messiah!" What would they say? What would they do!?

It seemed like a dream. It was one of those moments that is too good to be true but too astounding to be contrived. If nothing else, the splash of cold water in the baptistry reminded us just how real this was. If I should die in my sleep tonight, my life now has fulfillment and meaning. If I don't, then until my dying breath I'll do what I did today. I'll spend my life making disciples, for indeed Jesus is with us always, "even to the very end of the age." Now, at last, I understand.

Sincerely,

Matthew

May 25, A.D. 60

Brother Luke,

It is good to have you in our fair city. Although we wish it could be under different circumstances. Our prayers are with you, Aristarchus, and Paul, especially for their upcoming trials. Yet, we are confident that God's grace will continue to be upon you as it was through your trying trip last winter. The church rejoices that you fared better than the boat! Please know that the brothers and elders here consider you our guest and are prepared to meet your financial needs, even as you minister to the sick among us.

Well, on to the business at hand. In answer to your question, yes, the rumors you heard are true. I am one of the founding fathers of the church here (if that title can be justly used of anyone but God). Yes, our church is nearly as old as the one in Jerusalem. We grew a great deal when Peter preached for us after he escaped Herod Agrippa's fiendish ax. Nor can we fail to mention John Mark who served as his amanuensis after he left Paul and Barnabas' first tour. Yet both were here only a few short years, and even then the church was over a decade old.

It actually began shortly after Pentecost, following Jesus' resurrection. A rather large group of us who decided to go to Jerusalem that year. For some it was their very first pilgrimage. For the poorer families, it was the only time in their lives they would see the Holy city. That heightened our anticipation, of course. Those of us who had been before were willing tour guides. On route we recounted previous sojourns like generals of war swapping stories. No one seemed to mind. We had no way of knowing just how significant this particular trip would be.

To make a long story short, we were in the temple completing our sacrifices for ritual purification. It was the opening day of the feast so there was quite a bit of commotion. There were beggars at the entrance, merchants in the court of the Gentiles, family reunions in Solomon's colonnade, and thousands of priests officiating the sacrifices. Suddenly the customary commotion was upstaged by a band of Galileans parading into the temple. With them came the sound of a summer storm, yet there wasn't a cloud in the sky. To be honest, it gave me chills. I nearly bolted, but something told me this was not to be missed.

A handful of Galileans spread out across the colonnade and each began to preach in a different dialect. Naturally we gravitated to the speaker we understood. I heard about Jesus for the first time in Latin. This first message was just the prelude! Once they had the crowd's undivided attention, Peter got up and presented the Gospel. When he got to Psalm 110, I'll never forget it 'til the day I die! I can show you the very stone on which I stood. Like a ton of bricks it hit me: Oh Dear God, we killed your Son! I wasn't even there when it happened, yet somehow I knew that I too was culpable! We looked at each other, expecting lightening to strike at any time. Then we looked at Peter and cried, "What should we do?! Please tell us. We'll do it . . . anything!"

There was an urgency and a guilt that was pungent. I'll never forget Peter's response: "Repent and be baptized every one of you in the name of Jesus Christ for the forgiveness of your sins and you shall receive the gift of the Holy Spirit." I remember thinking to myself, "You've got to be kidding me! There is forgiveness for this? There is a way out?! I want in on it!" I wasn't the only one thinking that either. There was a mad rush to the Mikvehs outside the temple. Oh, not everyone was convinced, but I'd be a liar if I said there were less than 3,000 souls immersed that day!

At first it seemed like such a paltry act. Surely such a dastardly deed could not be undone by a ritual bath! But as I stood there in line and watched hundreds of others give their lives to Christ, it struck me. This is not a ritual bath, it is a re-enactment of the death, burial and resurrection of Jesus. As Paul said in his letter several years ago: "Do you not know that all of us who have been baptized into Christ Jesus were baptized into his death? We were buried therefore with him by baptism into death, so that as Christ was raised from the dead by the glory of the Father, we too might walk in newness of life" (Rom 6:3-4).

This was the end of my life as I knew it and the beginning of my slavery to Christ. As the seriousness of the moment blossomed in my mind, it only strengthened my resolve to accept Jesus as Lord and Christ.

Needless to say, the rest of the week was spent in the temple asking questions of the Apostles, celebrating the Eucharist, meeting together and praying. Our decisions to become Christians were bolstered by two great signs. First, the Apostles laid their hands on the sick and they became well. Never since have I seen such an outpouring of the power of God, nor have I needed to. The reality of those days forever lives in my memory as evidence of the truth of Christianity. Second, and perhaps more important still, the believers collected their assets and voluntarily surrendered their surplus to alleviate the suffering of the poor among them. It was as if they had become a new family in which none of the children were allowed to go hungry.

The week too quickly came to a close. We pleaded with the Apostles to send a representative here to Rome to do what they did there. (As if the Holy Spirit could be transported and his power reproduced!) They said Jesus hadn't given them leave of the city just yet. We begged, but to no avail. "How then shall we carry on?" we asked, "What shall we do?" To this they replied, "Do what you have done for the past seven days: Adhere to the teachings of the Scriptures and the Apostles, meet together regularly to encourage and support each other, and when you meet, remember Jesus' death for you through a memorial meal, and above all, pray." So that's what we did when we returned home. Our friends and neighbors soon took notice, and the rest is His-story.

Sincerely,

Andronicus (Rom 16:7)

My Witnesses

July 4, A. D. 60

Dr. Luke,

I had heard rumors that you were collecting information about the early church while you were waiting for Paul's trial under Felix. With the governor's continued delays (no great surprise for those of us who have had to endure his rule!), I was afraid that you would eventually get to me. Don't get me wrong, I'm not ashamed of my story. God is my witness how I have been witness to God's grace. My problem is, to be brutally honest, I'm a bit intimidated by your reputation as a scholar. I know I shouldn't be since we are brothers in Christ, but I am a bumpkin compared to you. You know I was lame for the first forty years of my life; I didn't get to go to school. So if my words are simple and my grammar incorrect, please pardon this simpleton. I may be a simple man, but what happened to me is significant.

It was a quarter of a century ago. I wasted away my days laying at the gate of the temple. I couldn't work, or study, or, worst of all, worship! Do you know how frustrating it is to love God with all your heart and not be allowed in?! (Perhaps as one of the Goüm you do). I was SO close, right at the gate! Every day people would walk right past me, sometimes right over me into God's house. Except for the few who tossed pocket change in my cup, as if they could buy God's grace, most never even noticed me. Or at least they acted like they didn't. But I noticed them. Hypocrites! I would have dragged myself a hundred miles to worship God. They walked in with such ease, and so carelessly into the Lord's presence. I don't mean to sound arrogant, but when you look up from the ground, you see more clearly the honor God deserves.

Well, one day I was sitting at the Nicanor gate. That's where my friends usually put me if we could beat the other beggars to the spot. It was a beautiful gate. Forty five foot high double doors of solid brass. The splendor of the gate made an impressive contrast to the riffraff at its base. We were a motley crew of bandaged beggars with open sores, crutches, and jingling tin cups. We were a sight! But our sound was even more pathetic. We were practiced at getting pity. Our constant groans even irritated ourselves . . . but it worked.

It was about three in the afternoon. That's rush hour at the temple, when people come for their afternoon prayers and the evening sacrifice. Man, we were workin' the crowd. Most people rushed pass, pretending not to see. I tried to catch people's eye when they tried to sneak a peak at the freak show at their feet. When someone did look at me I gave them that sad puppy look and said with a moan, "Mister, can you spare some change?"

Two of those Galileans walked by. I caught their eyes and began to work my magic. They stopped and stared at me. Not one of those curious "what's-wrong-with-him" looks. Rather, it felt like he was looking into my soul, the way two lovers do, or a mother with an infant. It made me uncomfortable. I wasn't used to being treated like a human being. It kind of stung. So I looked away.

Then the bold one said, "Look at me man!" I perked up, sure he was going to give me some money. Besides, I knew who these guys were. They were the leaders of that new sect that followed Jesus. It hadn't been that long since I overheard Jesus' preaching as I sat there at the gate. He said the most amazing things and in the most amazing way. Had I had legs, I believe I would have followed him too. I was disappointed when I heard he had been executed by the Romans as a rabble rouser. But it was no big loss for me. I had no investment in the guy. Just a few days later, there was this rumor that he had risen from the dead. Most people I knew said it was a silly superstition that only a bunch of backwoods Galileans would buy. Others seemed to think it was so. Some, in fact, were so sold on the movement that they sold their property and gave it to Jesus' head guys to give to the poor among them. But what did I care who was right? I was just interested in their surplus. As Peter stared me down, I thought to myself, "He's got the keys to Apostolic cash." I needed some!

I could hardly believe what I heard: "Silver or gold I do not have, but what I have I give you. In the name of Jesus Christ of

Nazareth, walk." I thought the guy was nuts. Before I knew what had happened, he snatched my hand and jerked me to my feet. It was one of those slow motion moments, if you know what I mean. I remember thinking, "My legs are gonna buckle like noodles and I'm gonna fall flat on my face. I'll be the laughing stock of the Temple. I'll sue this sucker for every benevolent penny he's got!"

As my feet hit the pavement, this sensation shot through my ankles and up to my knees. It wasn't pain. It wasn't fire. The best I can describe is that it was like light that overcame a darkness in my body. My first few steps were tentative, like a newborn fawn. Then, uncontrollably, unconsciously, I started to hop, skip, and jump around. Before I knew it, I was in the middle of the temple. I had never been there before, you understand. But I barely even noticed. All I knew was that I was lame all my life, and now I could walk. This changed everything! I was now normal. No, wait, I was super-normal.

I created quite a stir. But like I said, I had never been in the temple before. How was I to know that you're not supposed to run in church? It wasn't long before I had attracted a crowd. I heard what they were saying, "It looks like the same guy; but it just can't be!" Then one fellow in the back said, "It can be! . . . It is!" When I turned to see who said this, I recognized the man. He used to beg beside me when he was blind. Now we serve communion together on Sundays.

I stood proudly next to Peter and John, shouting, "Listen to these men! Hear what they did for me!" At that point I got out of the way and turned the spotlight over to Peter. Oddly enough, Peter got out of the way too, and gave the spotlight over to Jesus. He preached for a good three hours about how Jesus was killed by our people, but how God raised him for our justification. I hung on their words even more closely than I clung to their sides.

The Jewish big wigs (Annas, Caiaphas, John, Alexander, *et. al.*) didn't appreciate Peter's sermon as much as the rest of us. In fact, as day gave way to dusk, they couldn't stand it any longer. The guards arrested us. Normally, I would have been irate and terrified. But that night, I didn't want to be anywhere else but with these two men, even if it was in a jail. Besides, what were they going to convict me of? Jay walking?! Disturbing the peace, perhaps. Well, that's my story of how I joined the church, and I'm stickin' with it.

Standing for Him,

Simeon Ben Jacob (AKA *Hallomenos*)

My Witnesses

A PRESS RELEASE ON THE GALILEANS: (7/16/34)

From: Alexander Ben Jeremias

Two days ago there was a significant disturbance in our city. Simeon Ben Jacob, who had been lame from birth was healed by God at the temple. Two of the infamous Galileans, Peter Bar Jonas and Johanan Bar Alphaeus happened on the wondrous occurrence and blasphemously took credit for the divine healing, robbing glory due to the Divine Majesty. They were arrested, according to our law, and warned concerning their transgression. The teachers of the law carefully explained to them their error, and they were strictly ordered not to preach heresy anymore or they would suffer the penalty of God's law – death. If anyone has information concerning further blasphemous infractions, they are to report it to the authorities immediately.

We realize that our actions may seem harsh. Please know that we take most seriously such heresy that spreads like gangrene among our people. These are difficult days for us Jews. We long for Messiah, and many pretenders capitalize on the weak-willed and mentally feeble in order to promote themselves for personal gain and self-aggrandizement. We are the shepherds of the people and will deal most vigilantly with wolves of deception. May all Israel understand, these so-called Christians are false teachers, leaders of a most pernicious cult. Many have fallen prey to their deceptive doctrines (some report up to 5,000 men). We pray to God-Almighty that the following public response will once and for all put to rest this plague of lies.

(1) Jesus Ben Joseph (so called) was a bastard from Galilee, the seed-bed of rebellions and criminals. He was crucified by Pontius Pilate because he was a threat to Roman security. He refused to pay taxes to Rome, he stirred up rebellions both in our city and around Palestine, and most serious of all, he claimed to be a king. Our high priest, Caiaphas, correctly said that this man must die for the security of our people. These heretics have tried to blame the leaders of Israel for his death. Be it known to all

Israel, that this man's death was his own doing, a result of his dangerous and irresponsible teaching.

(2) This cult of Galileans claims that Jesus was raised from the dead. This is a thing both contrary to nature and the sovereign will of God. We have sworn affidavits by the guards stationed at the tomb. They reported a robbery, obviously perpetrated by some of these Christians. It is a hoax of colossal proportions and a gruesome act of deception. These men defiled themselves and our nation when they entered the tomb of Joseph of Arimathea, manhandled the corpse and drug it off to who knows where, to do who knows what with it. We in the Sanhedrin are horrified by such a Godless and barbarous act. Our silence on this issue up until now has merely been due to sheer shock and horror at the depravity of these Galileans.

(3) These evil doers blaspheme in the worst imaginable way. Jesus was an illegitimate rebel, publically crucified in shame, an embarrassment and a danger to our people. In their cult, he is worshiped as God. Not only is this ludicrous, it is blasphemy deserving of death.

(4) Just like their dead leader, these men make a mockery of the temple. The disturbance of two days ago was outrageous and viewed unfavorably by Pilate's troops. If such riotous behavior continues, these Galileans will jeopardize the peace of our people and the very worship of God in his Holy Temple.

(5) They alter our ancient customs, handed down through Moses to our forefathers. They gather for their cultic meetings on the first day of the week when the Lord God ordained that we should busy ourselves with work. They are lazy and unwise, selling their assets to support the sluggards that they attract to themselves. Even their leaders have abandoned their noble occupations of fishing to come down here and stir up trouble in the capital city. It is even reported that among their meetings, they practice a ritual cannibalism with the crucified remains of their "god." We shudder to think that this was likely their motive for robbing Joseph's grave. They have asked us to produce Jesus' body if we think we can; we would ask them NOT to do so.

My Witnesses

(6) These Galileans are ignorant buffoons, unschooled and unsophisticated. They attract to themselves people of like mind. They neither know the law nor respect our traditions. Do not follow them or you will endanger your own standing in the synagogue as well as that of your family.

If you have any questions about "The Way" or if you have information concerning their illegal activities, please contact the captain of the temple guard, John of Jericho, Saul of Tarsus or myself. May the truth of God prevail and the people of Israel prosper. *Shalom.*

August 22, A.D. 61

Brother Luke,

So my old friend Saul finally made it to Rome. I Praise God, except for his chains. If I know him, even in his old age he is reckless in his testimony, and revels in any opportunity to proclaim Christ, even if he is in custody. His dreams have finally come true, to preach the king of creation to the emperor of the world.

I'm sure he has told you much about our travels already. I'll not retrace his steps. Nor will I digress into our past disagreement. I trust he has represented our differences fairly and reasonably, so I feel no need to defend myself.

What I will tell you, however, is what Paul had no way of knowing. Not that our relationship does not precede the events I'm about to recount. Indeed, I would say we were "professional associates" in the synagogue of the Freedmen long before he gave his life to Christ. But while he and Stephen were debating Christianity among our Jewish brethren, Saul was obviously out of the loop concerning the meetings of The Way.

As for myself, I was convinced of the truth of Christianity as early as Pentecost. I was, however, marginal in my faith. Don't get me wrong. I was fully convinced in my mind, but my wallet had a ways to go before it caught up. In other words, my trust in Christ had not yet apprehended all areas of my life.

In those early days, the Apostles, Peter and John, were arrested by some delegates from the Sanhedrin. In fact, to be fair-minded, you might want to locate a copy of a press release by Alexander Ben Jeremias, dating from the summer of 34. That will explain the official Jewish position, at least of the antagonistic leaders. Nonetheless, their objections to our movement are easily answered. Their venom and faithless accusations are obviously untenable propaganda. The truth of the matter is that Peter and John, who have never been trained in oratory or dialectic, confounded the entire council. The high priest was not just tongue-tied, he was hog-tied (and that's a pretty bad thing for a Jew!). It was obvious by the Apostle's wisdom and demeanor that they had been students of the great Master.

Because the council's logic and theology were impotent in the face of historic fact and God's truth, the only recourse left to them was "legal" threat. Their actions had the form of jurisprudence, but the heart of persecution. I remember well the day they came back to the prayer meeting with a full report. We gasped when Peter said, "They threatened us with capital punishment if we continued to preach in the name of Jesus." After an uncomfortable pause, one of the disciples asked, "What are you going to do?" Peter laughed, but it somehow had the tone of a rebuke. "What will we do!? . . . What will we do!!? . . . Why we will preach, that's what we will do. Can we afford to obey men's orders when they contravene God's? Never again will I allow my own security to cloud my confession of Christ." At that he paused, blinked, and swallowed. He was going to press on, but the memory was just too heavy. Instead, he began to pray.

It was the most moving prayer I think I had ever heard in my life. I couldn't tell whether he was preaching to us, or talking to God. Perhaps it was both. I do remember that he fully exegeted Psalm 2:1-2. It was the first time I heard a Christian pray curses on his enemies. It gave me the chills, I'll tell you.

Then it happened. The entire place was shaken. It felt like an earthquake. But after inquiring of our neighbors, we realized it was localized in our own house. That's what did it for me! That turned a corner on my faith. When God starts to respond before you finish praying, you are part of something worth dying for. And if it is worth dying for, then it is worth living for. And if its worth living for its worth **giving** for. I was now ready to put my money where my mouth was.

In those early days, there was an uncanny sense of family among the believers. If one member was suffering we all suffered with them. Then it struck me: There is no excuse for the body to suffer when I have the personal assets to meet the need! I know it sounds crazy, and it probably was not wise financially, but I could do nothing else. Besides, even after selling my property I still had plenty to live on, although my IRA was shot. I didn't care; I still don't! Our God has more than supplied my needs.

Luke, I know you know this joy because you are a physician. When I watched the Apostles dole out food and clothes to the poor among us, my heart skirted the boundaries of heaven. My eyes were so clouded with tears that I couldn't see theirs. But I heard the surprised gasps of women and orphans, of men without work, and pilgrims who fell on hard times. I still have their thank-you letters in my files. My greatest joy, though, was the train of Christians who followed my example. Not all their motives turned out to be pure, but the great majority of them were. I do hope this doesn't sound arrogant, but I just love being a catalyst for good, and an encourager of the weak.

Luke, I have so many happy memories: Running as a child through the fertile fields of Cyprus, traveling with Saul, the reconciliation of John Mark, the victory for the Gentiles at the Jerusalem council, and on they go. But I think my happiest memory of all was the day I sold out to Jesus and watched my wealth make an eternal investment in heaven. I know it may sound strange, but never before nor since have I felt more like Jesus.

Because of Him,

Joseph the Levite (AKA Barnabas)

An Interview with Nicanor
(March 7, A.D. 58)

Luke: What can you tell us about God's first murder of his own people?

Nicanor: First of all, let's not make God out to be the bad guy. Secondly, this was not the first time God's discipline of his people resulted in the death of His own. Surely you remember Achan of old who confiscated some gold. Like Achan, Ananias and Sapphira halted the progress of God's people into the promised land. This was the very first blemish on the bride of Christ. Up to this point she was pristine. God's lethal response is indicative of his zealous love for the church, not merely his repugnance at one man's irreverence.

Luke: What exactly happened?

Nicanor: Well, those were the best of times for the church. Everything you've heard was true. We had daily communion services in our house churches. We zealously devoted ourselves to the study of the Scriptures, especially the Psalms and Prophets. Our prayer meetings literally "rocked". Our benevolence was unbelievable! It embodied the very best about the church. I remember when Joseph sold a significant piece of property and laid the proceeds at the Apostles' feet to distribute to the poor. That started a stream of giving that flows to this day. It wasn't long before "Barnabas" was a household name.

Luke: Was that what prompted Ananias and Sapphira? The desire for recognition, I mean?

Nicanor: It is hard to psychoanalyze a dead man, but that is probably a pretty good guess. I have to say, however, if that was his motive, none of us are too far away from him. I think that's what struck us most.

Luke: Many Christians will ask what was so wrong with what they did.

Nicanor: Yes. When we look at the surface, it seems to be a trivial sin. But look deeper. Ananias and Sapphira were trying to serve two masters, God and money. Jesus said that was impossible! You will always wind up loving only one. Ananias wanted the praise of men as well as the luxury of material goods. God got left out, in one sense, but in another sense, God was used as a stepping stone to self-satisfaction. God refuses to be used as a means to satisfy men's petty pursuits! Indeed, Ananias and Sapphira were very much like Iscariot. Satan duped them both through the purse to commit blasphemy that damaged the body of our Lord.

Luke: So how was their plot discovered?

Nicanor: Well, after the bill of sale had been signed, Sapphira headed off to the market with a wad of cash. Ananias came to the prayer meeting with the other half. When he laid it at Peter's feet, it appeared to me that he glanced over his shoulder to see who was watching. Then he said, with a deep rich tone: "Praise be to God, the giver of all good gifts. Here is the overflow of the Lord's bounty." The crowd was electrified. It was like "Barnabas, the sequel." Peter was the only one who wasn't so happy. He stared hard at Ananias and asked, "So you are saying that this is the full purchase price?" "Indeed," he replied.

Peter now looked hard toward the floor. It got deadly quiet in the room. After what seemed like an eternity, Peter glared at Ananias with both fire and pathos. "How could you?!" he cried. "How is it that you allowed Satan to infiltrate your heart and mind? Didn't you own the property before you sold it? Didn't you control the money after you sold it? No one held a knife to your throat. Yet you have lied, not to men, but to the Spirit of God! You will surely pay a high price for your deception."

Luke: What happened next?

Nicanor: Ananias fell to the floor. At first we thought he had just passed out. I mean, who would imagine that God was that serious about holiness?! We just stood there and stared at him. No one wanted to touch him lest God's judgment was contagious. You should have seen Peter; he was incredulous. He pointed at five young men and said, "Gentlemen, get him out of here! Bury him in a shallow grave like the pauper he his." Then I realized that one of the names Peter called was my own. I moved forward slowly, numbly. At first I wasn't sure whether it was a dream or not. But as his body began to bloat in the warm Palestinian sun, we understood just how real it was.

Luke: What did you guys talk about as you worked?

Nicanor: Absolutely nothing!!! We were dumbstruck. Yet a million thoughts raced through our minds: Who is next? Why did I escape when my sin is just as bad? What is going to happen to the church? Will this scare everyone off? Will more people be killed? What we eventually found was that the fear of God only leads to the growth of his body. We need not pander to people's "sensibilities." We need to fear this God of love who himself loves holiness as much as he loves his children. But mostly we thought, "Shouldn't someone tell Sapphira?" Yet no one dared interrupt his own introspection.

Luke: So how did she find out?

Nicanor: That was interesting. It took us about three hours to complete our dreadful task. Meanwhile, Sapphira returned from the market. Her new dress betrayed her. Peter asked her about the purchase price of the property. She obviously had no idea what had just happened to her husband. Everyone held their breath. They wanted to blurt out, "Don't do it!" Yet they dared not interfere. She was obviously caught on the horns of a dilemma. Her face gave her away. She was a poor liar who lied too easily. If she told the truth, she would have to admit her husband was dishonest. I'm sure in her mind, she felt it would be too difficult to live with Ananias if she dishonored him publicly. Little did she know she would die with him if she didn't. I didn't hear her say it personally, but the moment we opened the door, she hit the deck. We had a second silent funeral. Fear seized the whole church. I'll tell you this, before we entered the house again, we knocked.

My Witnesses

A STUDENT MEMO   (9/15/34)

From: Gamaliel
To: Saul
Subject: The Sect of the Nazarenes

Your objections to my "support" of the Nazarenes were stated forcefully and articulated clearly, even if they could have been tempered with a bit more kindness and respect. Please don't misunderstand; I was neither intimidated nor offended by your objections in class. Yet now, as always, I seek to be your mentor. So I want to take this opportunity to exhort you to listen more, talk less, and to be munificent with others, even your antagonists.

It was neither the time nor the place in our lecture hall to justify my defense of the Nazarenes. Yet I felt that such an advanced student as yourself deserved a thorough and thoughtful explanation.

As you remember, the Twelve were arrested after disobeying the Sanhedrin's explicit instructions not to preach about this Jesus anymore. I must say that this censorship made me a bit uncomfortable; not because I am opposed to silencing heresy and opting for the unrefereed free exchange of godless ideology. Rather, I was uncomfortable because it made the Sanhedrin look as if we could not respond to the **ideas** of the Galileans, and so used strong-arm tactics rather than logic, truth, and God's Word.

They were arrested and thrown in jail until a hearing could be arranged on the following day. According to just jurisprudence, these men were first warned and now it was time to prosecute. Yet remember the real issue at hand – the healing of Simeon Ben Jacob (*Hallomenos*). Obviously, the official stance of the Sanhedrin was that this healing was only coincidentally related to the Galileans. Yet there were many among our leaders who were not convinced (one way or the other). In other words, the Nazarenes were threatened due to circumstantial evidence the first time. In my mind, that made their second arrest tenuous to begin with. This demanded that I proceed with caution.

One thing we all agreed on was that a miracle of such proportion could only be accomplished by God. If we assume, even for a moment, that it was, in fact, done through the hands of the Galileans, then our own position is precarious. Again, based on this possibility, I urged a position of tentative caution. Furthermore, the escape of the Twelve from prison is mysterious! They claimed it was an angel that released them. The Sadducees obviously scoffed. But you and I believe in angels. So theoretically, we must admit the possibility of their honesty. Furthermore, each guard, to a man, denied any plot on behalf of the Galileans. After careful investigation, there was no concrete evidence that any of them had conspired with the sect. Do you see now why we must not jump to hasty conclusions?

You have accused me of being untrue to Judaism. Why? Do you not believe in angels and miraculous healings? Do you not know your Jewish history of God working through strange and even pagan peoples? Read again of Balaam, Melchizedek, Jonah, Joseph's Pharaoh and a host of others. In fact, I am only acting as a responsible Pharisee. You, my friend, are the one being swayed, yes, even by the Sadducees. They are the ones who deny angels, healings and the hope of Messiah. Haven't you paid attention to the real impetus behind this prosecution? It is the Sadducees who fear losing control of the temple. It is their jealous rage and petty protection of their positions that instigated this. I urge you to reconsider whose side you are really on.

Furthermore, the movement of the Nazarenes is growing in influence. This has not escaped the notice of the Roman peace-keeping forces. The whole city is on pins and needles. If we treat the Nazarenes' leaders harshly, what will prevent a riot? I wasn't so interested in sparing their lives as if I was their friend and protector. No, my purpose was broader. I am trying to spare our city. More than that, I hope to salvage the integrity of the Shepherds of Israel. Such tense times call for intense caution, my son.

One last thing. If you want to do a favor for a sect, make martyrs out of their leaders. That will surely inflame their followers. They will cling more tenaciously than ever to their error. You are a good student of history, Saul. Remember Theudas who led away four hundred of our people? He was killed and his followers disbanded and were never heard from again. And what about Judas who revolted during the census? Likewise, he was killed and his followers went their own way. The point is: If this movement is the efforts of mere men, it will fade as the others have. Let God do the killing. Saul, you don't need to defend God. He can hold his own ground! If, however, this movement is from God, if Jesus is raised from the dead as they claim, you wouldn't want to meet him in the noonday sun. One would be a colossal fool to oppose God, and the chief of all sinners to slay His children.

Be cautious, my friend. Don't allow the fire in your heart to blind you eyes. Rage against men is never an appropriate barometer of our love for God. Don't follow the Sadducees who cry out for their death. God is seldom in as much a rush to vindicate himself as we are. I am not, as you say, swayed by the fishermen. Nevertheless, Peter Bar Jonah spoke truth when he said, "We must obey God, rather than men."

September 6, A.D. 34

Dear Mom and Dad,

This is the most difficult letter I've ever had to write because I know it is going to break your hearts. Yet I write with overwhelming joy. What Benjamin told you is true. I am a Christian. You may now consider me dead, but let me assure you that I have never before been so alive. Furthermore, I don't consider myself to have forsaken our religion. On the contrary, I have found our Messiah. I do not write to say "goodbye" to you whom I love with all my heart. I write to tell you the greatest news: Our sins are forgiven and we can once again walk with God as Adam did in the garden.

As I have been arguing in the synagogue of the Freedmen, Jesus fulfills the words of our prophets. Consider Psalm 16:10, "You will not abandon me to the grave, nor will you let your Holy One see decay." Surely you can't believe that David wrote of himself! It must be another. The Apostles are eyewitnesses to this man Jesus whom God raised after having lain in Joseph's tomb for three days. The Chief Priests have yet to produce a body or give a reasonable explanation for the empty tomb. Can you not see? This was God's foreordained plan.

Tell me, what is the meaning of Isaiah 53, the suffering servant? This cannot refer to a nation nor an era, but must refer to our Messiah. It was Jesus who stepped into our place. We are headed to the slaughter unless we accept his death for ours. Father, I've been to the daily sacrifice with you too many times not to know your heart. I've seen in your eyes that look of desperation. I know that you know that the blood of bulls and goats cannot undo our deeds. Only the God-man can redeem our mutiny against the Living One.

Or what do you say about Psalm 110:1 "The Lord says to my Lord . . ."? How can David refer to the Messiah as "Lord" when he is David's own descendant? Since when is the descendant considered master of the Father? I'll tell you: when the descendant descends from on high! Jesus was born of a virgin, impregnated by the power of the Holy Spirit. If you refuse to believe this truth, the second half of Psalm 110:1 must fall heavy on your heart: "until I make your enemies a footstool for your feet." The stakes are terribly high. Please do not turn away from the truth.

These and a hundred other passages predict Jesus as the Christ of God. Indeed Saul of Tarsus has tried to refute the Word of God. But look closely and you will see that his venom is supported not by logic or truth but by jealous rage and trumped-up witnesses. He stirs up dissension and gossips his way into men's hearts. You know that I do not stand alone in my belief that Jesus is the Christ. Hundreds of priests have obeyed the Gospel here in our own city.

Not only is the Gospel verified by the Scriptures and the multitudes that are won over daily, but it is also confirmed by the very finger of God. I hesitate to bring this up lest it seem like idle boasting, but it is the truth. There are dozens of people who were healed by my own hands. Believe me, I was as surprised and delighted as they. Those who had been blind, paralyzed, dumb, demonized, distorted with every imaginable illness, they are healed through the Apostles and those of us on whom they laid their hands. Don't just take *my* word for it. Ask the physicians in Jerusalem who are looking for work!

There is one other evidence I want to lay before you. It is the unity of the church. In recent days there was a dispute among the believers. We have a reputation, you know, of feeding the poor among us. Well, some people felt that the Grecian widows were being slighted. Apparently the rampant discrimination of Jerusalem Jews had reared its ugly head in the church of Jesus Christ. The Apostles had no intent of neglecting anyone, of course. But our numbers had grown so quickly it was next to impossible to keep up with the administrative needs of benevolence. They decided to delegate seven men who would serve as ambassadors of benevolence. The congregation put it to a vote and my name was one that was chosen. Two things impressed me about this. First, all seven of us are Grecian Jews. It is as if the congregation was saying, "We would rather have unity than egalitarianism." Where else, Father, will you find people denying themselves for the sake of others? You know as well as I do that men's hearts are not so moved. Only the Holy Spirit of God could transform us like that. Second, they only chose men who were full of the Spirit and wisdom. This was no popularity contest. It was no political maneuver. The church had a need, and they chose the men most qualified to meet that need. They chose men who were already actively serving the body. Moreover, they chose men qualified to communicate the gospel, because our task is more than distributing food. We are bearers of the bread of life.

Abba, I can hear the wheels turning in your head even as I write. I know that you love the Scriptures and will give careful consideration to their testimony about Jesus. I know you are a man of reason. The miracles from my hands, the conversions of thousands and the unity of the church will not escape your notice. But I also know that you are a practical man, cautious and protective of your family. "Be careful!" I can hear you say. Father, I am sorry, but this time I cannot heed your advice. If being careful means being silent, then no. They have not yet killed anyone except our Lord, Jesus. But many of us are willing to follow in his steps. All my life I've proudly followed in your steps. Now I beg of you to follow in mine. Accept Jesus as Messiah.

Love,

Stephen

My Witnesses

June 20, A.D. 39

To: Gabriel Ben Zachi and Anna
From: Saul of Tarsus

Grace to you and peace from God our Father and the Lord Jesus Christ, through whom we have the forgiveness of our sins.

This is the most difficult letter that I've ever had to write. I was hoping to share all this with you face to face when I was in Jerusalem. My trip was cut short when the Lord Jesus appeared to me in a vision and ordered me to leave the city. In fact, I was only in Jerusalem fifteen days and only got well acquainted with Cephas, James, and Barnabas. So I'm afraid that my apology must be reduced to writing.

I've run through these words a thousand times over the last three years. Yet no turn of phrase adequately expresses my remorse. I can only beg you to hear my heart. Gabriel and Anna, it was I, Saul of Tarsus who held the cloaks at your son's execution. It was I who argued with him in the synagogue of the Freedmen. It was I who trumped up false charges and stirred up false testimony. I am responsible for the death of your son. I, the chief of sinners, know that God has forgiven me through the grace of Christ, for whose death I also cried. We all have regrets in life, moments that we would like to snatch back, yet none more than I. How I long to undo those two moments when I chanted "Crucify Him" . . . "Stone him"! My greatest fear is that the annals of history will remember me most as the murderer of the first Christian martyr.

How can I ask you to pardon me? Only because you are now my brother and sister in Christ. I am laid bare before you. I beg you to forgive me.

Please know that Stephen's death was not in vain. In fact, during my three days of blindness it was his voice that I heard in my head. Since my conversion I can't tell you how many times I've used his arguments, how many times I've presented his Christian interpretation of Old Testament prophecies. His

-35-

testimony was profound. He stood valiantly in the face of lethal opposition with the face of an angel. He demonstrated how Christians were true to Judaism. They blasphemed neither God nor Moses, neither the Temple nor the Law. In fact, his history lesson proved how the righteous of God were always persecuted by the mainstream religious establishment of Judaism. From Abraham to Joseph, from Moses to David, many of our patriarchs foreshadowed the Christ. All of our national history pointed to this one man, Jesus. Even as an unbeliever, I marveled at Stephen's clarity and dignity. He reminded me so much of Jesus.

I can assure you that my unrighteous actions were prompted by righteous indignation. I have lived with a clear conscience up to this very day. I was convinced that I was doing God a favor and preserving our nation when I destroyed the "heretics." But your son was right when he accused us: "You stiff-necked people, with uncircumcised hearts and ears! You are just like your fathers. You always resist the Holy Spirit!" My, how history repeats itself!

I was so furious that I clenched my fists, gritted my teeth, and began to chant, "Death to the heretic!" Yet as I looked at him I was nearly halted in my tracks by his innocence and purity. He just stood there looking up into the sky. Then he said it. "Look, I see heaven open and the Son of Man standing at the right hand of God." At the time his words appeared to me to be pure impudence. How dare he suggest that Jesus was with God. How dare he suggest that He stood as judge over ME. I now regret not looking to the sky to see if there was any truth in his claim. I may not have been allowed to see what he saw, but I wish I had at least tried.

I'm embarrassed to tell you how inflamed I became. Like fitful children we covered our ears and shouted at the top of our lungs as if to say, "We can't hear you . . . We're not listening!" In but a moment's time he was dragged outside the city walls so as to make for a Kosher killing. Yes, it was illegal, at least according to the Romans, who had stripped us of capital. That's why it was so risky for me to hold the cloaks, taking responsibility for the mob's actions. I was young and impetuous, and very proud that it was I who drew first blood. How our pride can turn to shame. My crowning moment now smells like sulfur. How Satan can deceive us, especially when he comes in clerical robes!

I wish I could say that your son died a painless death, that it was quick and easy. That would be a lie. If you've never seen a stoning, pray God spares you. Even the cruelest of men or the most zealous of crusaders are taken aback by the first solid blow and the splattering of blood. I don't say this to add pain to your soul, but to tell you that even in the crucible, your son mirrored Jesus. I was witness to both deaths. Even then I noticed how Stephen had incorporated the Master's ideas and attitudes. His dying words were these two lines from the lips of the Master: "Lord Jesus, receive my spirit" and "Lord, do not hold this sin against them." Perhaps this is how I could beg your forgiveness; it was your son's dying wish.

Stephen was a persuasive preacher and a valiant martyr. Should it be God's will, I could hope to follow in his footsteps on both counts. The grace of the Lord Jesus Christ be with your Spirit. Amen.

April 14, A.D. 57

Brother Luke,

The next time you see Paul, tell him I said, "I told you so!" What was it? Two weeks ago? We both begged him not to go up to Jerusalem. Even at Mnason's house, you remember the conversations (behind Paul's back). We knew it would come to this. I had no idea, however, that he would be back here in chains so quickly. Frankly, I'm concerned for Paul's safety under Felix.

Wait a minute. Did you hear what I just said? "I'm concerned for Paul's safety." Wow! There was a time when I hardly could have felt such a sentiment. You probably don't know this, Luke, but it was our brother Paul (Saul), who first chased me from house and home. That's right. As a young man, I too lived in Jerusalem. It seems so long ago now. I'm not complaining, mind you. Caesarea has been good to me these twenty-plus years. It's given me a beautiful wife and four precious daughters, themselves gifted by God to prophesy. What a trek it's been.

In those early days I was selected by the congregation as one of seven deacons who would help distribute food to our widows. The Apostles themselves laid their hands on us, and we began to perform miracles. That didn't get us in as much trouble as our preaching, however. Stephen was the most outspoken. He was to the deacons what Peter was to the Apostles. I don't suppose Paul has talked too much about him. He was the first to share in our Lord's suffering and inheritance. I still miss him.

Well, after Saul's vigilante zeal was consummated in Stephen's execution, he sought out the rest of us. I knew I was a prime target. After all, like Stephen, I was a Hellenistic Jew. Like Stephen, I was a high-profile deacon. And like Stephen, I was considered a leader among the believers from the synagogue of the Freedmen. I ran. It was not that I was afraid to die; it just seemed pretty pointless at that time. So I fled to where I knew Saul would never find me — Samaria. I felt as out of place as a hot-dog vender at Passover. All my life I was taught to fear and hate these "half-breeds" who corrupted the Word of God. I was even a bit smug as I walked past the ruins of their illicit temple atop Mt. Gerezim. I'm afraid the walls of my racism didn't crumble as easily as their shrine. I felt dirty and arrogant and afraid all at the same time. It was then that God spoke. I didn't hear him with my ears but more with my eyes. To my arrogance God said, "Are not these people mine as well, fashioned by my loving hand?" To my fear he said, "I am still on the throne, even in a distant land." And to my guilt he said, "You are right to feel dirty. But your guilt is misplaced. Rather than feel shame over living among Samaritans, you should feel shame for rejecting them." Isaiah 49:6 echoed in my mind, "It is too small a thing for you to be my servant to restore the tribes of Jacob and bring back those of Israel I have kept. I will also make you a light for the Gentiles that you may bring my salvation to the ends of the earth." Then I understood. We were not scattered by the avarice of a wicked man. We were scattered by the compelling love of God who yearns for all peoples to know him. So goes the story of the early church. We were anything but willing missionaries. We tried to stay in familiar territory and comfortable settings. But God's love wouldn't allow it. I suppose it will be thus until the end of time — the world will be reached by those of us with God's footprint imprinted on our backside.

What else could I do but tell them the good news of Jesus? I was as shocked at their acceptance as they were at my miracles. Yet I shouldn't have been. Was it not the Samaritans who first confessed Jesus as "The Savior of the World" (Jn 4:42)? Even so, I wasn't the only one who had a hard time believing it. The Apostles sent Peter and John to check it out. It was a good thing too. When they laid their hands on the brothers, they received miraculous powers just as Stephen and I had. No longer could this church be mistaken for the misguided zeal of a wayward deacon. The Apostles were the conduit through which God's grace fell full-force on the church. These miraculous gifts did in Samaria what Pentecost had done in Jerusalem. A church was born.

I would like to end the story here. Unfortunately, like most missionary ventures, there were complications. Undoubtedly you have heard of Simon Magus, the so-called "Great Power of God." He actually had the gall to ask Peter how much it would cost for him to be shown the secrets of this mystical power. Can you believe that?! He was equating the power of the Holy Spirit with his cultic arts which he neglected to leave in the baptistry. You should have been there. Peter wheeled around with a fire in his eyes I'd not seen since the Ananias incident. Only Simon was too dumb to know he should die on the spot. Peter said, "You can take your money to Hell with you." That was the last trouble we had with any Samaritan using the church for personal gain. Simon's influence in Samaria came to a screeching halt and he left town. You may get to meet him if you and Paul ever do get to Rome. I hear he is peddling himself among the naive Jet-set who delight in delusions.

I would have loved to stay in Samaria. It was a great ministry. There were large crowds and many miracles. But God moved me once again. I can honestly say I didn't mind even though I went from a booming church to a desert road. When God is your only audience, it is his presence that satisfies not numbers or accolades.

God moved me to a foreign city by the hand of persecution and my soul was satisfied in him. God moved me to a desert road by the voice of an angel and my soul was satisfied in him. God moved me to a metropolitan capital, miraculously transported by the breath of the Holy Spirit, and my soul was satisfied in him. Brother Luke, I know I'm not telling you anything new, but I suspect that Paul's predicament is controlled by a higher authority than Felix. If I know God, good will come from this. Find satisfaction in him.

His Servant,

Philip

OFFICIAL TRAVEL REPORT

To: Candace – Queen of the Ethiopians
From: Tumbasi, Secretary of the Treasury
RE: Journey to Jerusalem
Date: April 17, A.D. 36

May your dominion increase and your life prolong its years; may Jehovah, the God of the Hebrews, grant your kingdom peace.

Queen Candace, whom I serve with reverence and joy, please grant that your trusted eunuch may speak with candor. I am well aware of your skepticism about my interest in Judaism. "Why, pray tell," you asked, "would you travel to Jerusalem to worship with a bigoted race who exclude you from the very temple in which they pray to their God?" When I left, I had no answer for you. Indeed, I had no answer for myself. But God has granted his grace upon your servant. I return with an answer that is of more than academic interest to you. Please listen carefully, my Queen, as I appeal to you to seek the one true God, Jehovah, Lord of the Hebrews.

I went to the Temple in Jerusalem as usual. As usual, I was not allowed to enter the court of the men because, as they say, "You are a eunuch and not a man." It would be a lie to say I was not hurt and angered. My face showed no indignity, but deep inside my soul I wondered if they were right. I questioned not only my manhood but my humanity. That's what hurt the worst.

So why would I continue to go where I knew I would be rejected and humiliated? Because only here have I found the words of eternal life. Our own people know that our ancestral gods are superstition. The gods of the Egyptians are merely political tools to control the masses. The gods of the Greeks are creations of the poets to entertain the elite and satisfy the populous in their poverty. Candace, I speak with such candor because I know you respect my judgment. Your appointment has allowed me to travel the empire and see the religions of the world. They are mere vapors of superstition. Yet these Jews are different.

Their monotheism is compelling. The God of creation has spoken to their prophets who recorded His words in their sacred books. These contain wisdom that is beyond human sagacity and prophecies beyond human ability. Furthermore, their religion is more than a social construction for business and entertainment. It is ethical, moral and spiritual as well as political and social. Their business dealings are different, their families are different. In all, Judaism is the most noble of world religions to date.

Yet the problem remained: I was an outsider and would ever remain so due to my castration. Candace, please do not misunderstand. While castration carries with it notable regrets, your service has more than compensated for them. I love my job and I am proud of my heritage. I have no desire to leave your service, abandon my nation (the greatest on earth), or to change my skin and become Jewish. Yet my heart longs for God, the one true God who has revealed himself to this unlikely people. It is not them I desire, it is the God who has chosen them that I cannot live without. So you tell me, my Queen, where else could I go on this earth to pray to this God and hope to hear a word from him? Where else could I turn to seek to be included in his plan? Therefore, having no other recourse, I took my annual pilgrimage to the capital city of the Jews and, as always, I stood in the outer court to pray. I was pleased to be near my God, but deeply dissatisfied with mere proximity.

This trip was no different than all the rest. I went, I prayed, I left. But on my way out of the city, I purchased a handsome scroll of the prophet Isaiah (at a handsome price I might add). As I rode back home in my litter, I devoured the scroll as if it were honey. Less than half-way to Gaza I was already in chapter 53! I can't tell you how these words burned in my soul. I wanted to know of whom this prophet spoke. Was this part of the plan in which I could be included?

Suddenly, as if from nowhere on this desolate stretch, a Hellenistic Hebrew (a strange enough breed), ran along side my litter. He was so odd and out of breath that it didn't cross my mind that he might be God's messenger. He was difficult to ignore, especially when he began to inquire about my book. He didn't appear to be a promising Rabbi, but my options were somewhat limited at the time. So I invited him aboard.

Candace, the things I heard that day! I simply must tell you all, it is such good news! Nevertheless, this is not the place or the time. Suffice to say, beginning with Isaiah 53, this man named Philip wove together passages from all over the O.T. into a tapestry of eternal importance. For the first time religion made sense. No, it was more than that. Life made sense in Jesus, the Christ. As Isaiah 53 says, he died for our transgressions; we are free from the penalty of our sins. But that is just the beginning. He rose from the dead for our justification, opening up a new way for us to God. Did you hear what I said, O Queen? You and I as outsiders have a way in. It is through Jesus Christ. We find God, not in a temple in a distant country but in our own hearts. We don't search for Him, rather, he has come to us. I finally found what I had been looking for all my life!

As you can well imagine, I asked Philip how I could meet this Jesus since he had already returned to heaven. It was almost too simple and too good to be true: "Do you trust in Jesus Christ with all your heart? Do you accept him as Lord of your life?" I'm almost embarrassed to admit it but I squealed like a little child, "I do! I do!" "Well then," said he, "You should begin by imitating Jesus. You should be buried in water as he was in earth and raised as a new creature, reborn in him."

Just then I looked up and saw the pools of Bethsura. I ordered the chariots to stop. With quivering lips I asked if he would let me into Jesus. "I cannot," he said. My heart was crushed in an instant, but just as soon lifted when he continued, "Tumbasi, the invitation is not from me, but from Jesus Christ who accepts all men who trust him completely." Did you hear that, my Queen? He called me a man. Jesus Christ accepted me for who I was. He was perhaps the first person in my adult life to treat me as a human being. I will forever be his servant.

As we entered the water, I couldn't believe it was happening. This moment marked the end of my pilgrimage to God and the beginning of my adventure with him. As my body plunged beneath the waters I felt my whole history of evil being erased in the heavenlies. As I came up from the liquid tomb I thought I heard the beat of the wings of a dove. Then came the warmth, what you observed as a "glow." I can't explain it, I can only name it – the Holy Spirit. I was marked as God's man. I peered into the heavens. I didn't see it, but I heard it in my heart, the sound of my name being etched into the book of life. It is with tears of joy I write this account because I am now the chosen of God, the very bride of Christ, may he ever be praised.

I am well aware that this whole ordeal seems surrealistic (It's about to get worse). I would have loved to bring Philip here to verify my story and share with you the good news. But I was unable to locate him. Now Candace, you know that I am an accountant, a practical man not given to fits of fantasy. I am anything but gullible. My own servants will testify to the truth of what I am about to write. After I was immersed, I went to embrace Philip and caught nothing but air. I wiped the water out of my eyes; he was nowhere. I searched the bottom of the pool with my foot; he had not drowned. I inquired of my bodyguards, they saw nothing. We all came to this conclusion: I had been touched by an angel. I am prepared, with your support, of course, to publish my story to our entire nation. May your kingdom prosper in accordance with its promotion of the Kingdom of God.

MEMO

Date: August 15, A.D. 36
From: Jonathan Ben Amos
To: Caiaphas, High Priest
RE: Excommunication of Saul of Tarsus

Most honorable Caiaphas, I write concerning our recent expedition to Damascus. As you know, we set out with letters of extradition you gave us to ferret out the Nazarenes from their synagogues. Yet once we got to Damascus, Saul apparently had a nervous breakdown and turned over to the heretics. Gamaliel was apparently right – Saul's anger drove him insane.

Now, some will report to you that Saul had a vision of Jesus. That is a lie. Indeed, there was an unexplainable phenomenon, both a blinding light that knocked us to the ground, and a rumbling sound in the sky. But none of us, including Saul, saw any particular person, nor did we hear a discernible voice. We were all shaken, none more than Saul. The blinding light caused his eyes to scale over so that he could not see for several days. We escorted him to the home of Judas Ben Reuben, our contact in Damascus who first reported the growth of the insidious sect.

We were all on edge for those three days. Saul kept talking about this "vision" that none of the rest of us saw. We urged him to eat something but to no avail. His hunger only added to his dementia. Then our worst fears were realized. One Ananias Ben Gabriel arrived and began to feed Saul's delusion. He kept babbling about his own vision of Jesus and Saul's "commission by God" to preach to Gentiles, Kings, and Jews. Of all the nonsense! He spoke as if Saul would be the key to bringing Gentiles to the Kingdom of God. (He was apparently unaware of Saul's history, personality and training.) He had the audacity to say "The God of our fathers has chosen you to know his will and to see the Righteous One and to hear words from his mouth." We were horrified and speechless. The only thing he said that did make sense was that Saul would suffer greatly. If he continues on his present course, Ananias' prophecy is sure to come true.

Unexpectedly, the scales fell off Saul's eyes and he regained his sight. The physician Judas had hired to tend to Saul didn't know what to think since this case was so extraordinary. But we all agreed with his assessment, that this was a natural occurrence and not a divine healing. Nevertheless, Ananias, like most Nazarenes, was adept at taking advantage of these strange occurrences. He convinced Saul that his healing was a direct result of Jesus of Nazareth, the crucified rebel. Saul bought it, hook, line and sinker. He said, "Saul, why delay? Be immersed and wash away your sins, calling on Jesus' name."

It all happened so fast. Before we even thought of arresting Ananias, he had whisked Saul away. Understandably, it never occurred to us (until much later), that we should arrest the one who led us here to arrest others. It took us by surprise. And Saul took the synagogues of Damascus by surprise. His preaching was as persuasive as ever, only now he was arguing for the enemy. Great numbers apostatized. Without the threat of excommunication and extradition, the numbers of the Nazarenes swelled, although their leaders held Saul at arms length with understandable skepticism. It was then that we tried to hunt him down. Suddenly no one knew where he was. Our latest leads point to Arabia. It appears that Saul has fled our jurisdiction to escape punishment.

We have taken the liberty to write to King Aretas of Arabia as well as his appointed governor in Damascus, apprizing him of our concern as well as the political danger of "The Way." They assured us that they would support our efforts to find Saul and turn him over to the authorities in Jerusalem.

Caiaphas, here is the bottom line and the painful part of this letter. I recommend that Saul, when captured, be publically excommunicated and then executed if he refuses to recant. If this sounds harsh, please understand that I write this about my friend, class-mate and traveling companion. I am willing to fill the sandals left vacant by his apostasy. I am willing to testify against him before the Sanhedrin. I am even willing to cast the first stone, bringing upon my fallen brother the very punishment he initiated against the heretics. They deserved it then; Saul deserves it now. It is not that I am angry with Saul, rather I feel sorry for him. He has gone mad through his consuming anger. In his right mind, he would never have wanted to live this way. Now, as an act of mercy, I will spare my friend the embarrassment of gaining a reputation of being a disciple of Jesus. May our great God grant me resilience as I oppose all resistence.

Addendum: November 9, A.D. 39

After nearly three years in Arabia, Saul returned to Damascus, hoping we had forgotten his crime and apostasy. He was brazen enough to preach again in the synagogues. With the help of the governor, Judas Ben Reuben put out a warrant for his arrest. (There have been several men named Judas who were helpful in the resistence movement). Saul escaped, showing up later here in Jerusalem. Unfortunately, he was only here for about two weeks, and we were unable to apprehend him since he spent most of that time hunkered down with the Nazarenes. Some of these Christians still seem to think that Saul's conversion is a ruse, a sting to get at their inner leadership. That's too much to hope for. Most Christians have been emboldened by Saul's local appearance. I'm afraid we have lost much ground. I'm beginning to think that Gamaliel's advice to leave them alone was flawed.

We have heard reports that he has gone to visit his parents in Tarsus and so have sent informants there to try to discover his whereabouts. He is as slippery as that crucified rebel. But like his leader, his luck will one day run out. There are about forty of us who are dedicated to that end.

TWIN MIRACLES ROCK SHARON

Late last week, Simon Ben Jonas, the leader of the Jesus movement, paid a visit to the little town of Lydda. There he met a prospect named Aeneas Ben Solomon, who had been paralyzed for eight years. According to his father, Solomon Ben Zachri, he was injured in a construction accident when he fell from the top of a two-story building while completing the lattice work. This was a serious setback for the Solomon Construction Company, which at that time consisted of this father/son team. Solomon recalls, "The neighbors were kind, and patient with delays in building deadlines. However, I tell you, it was touch and go for six months. The greatest difficulty was not the business, but Aeneas' two young boys. I tried to help their mother with repairs and teaching the boys the trade. But even together, we were not an acceptable substitute for their father."

Just as this accident instantly changed Aeneas' life eight years ago, so Peter's visit instantly changed it again just three days ago. With surprisingly few details, Aeneas remembers the incident: "An old schoolmate of mine who had converted to Christianity about two years ago brought Peter to my house. He looked at me with a penetrating gaze, as if he were reading my soul or something. Then he said, 'Aeneas, Jesus Christ heals you. Get up and walk.' I felt a tingling sensation throughout my back and legs, then a surge of power that almost convulsed me. It was kind of like when you wake up and have an uncontrollable urge to stretch and then at the end of it you shake with the new-found strength of a night's rest. I rolled up my mat and hugged my family. I then embraced Jesus in faith. Ever since I've had a song in my heart and a hammer in my hand."

The most touching testimony comes from Aeneas Jr., the eldest boy: "My Bar-Mitzvah is next month. My dad never got to kick a ball with me, or race me to the market. But it will be worth it all just to watch him stand as I walk to the front of the Syna-gogue to read the scroll. But I guess even that means very little compared to what we've gained from all this – a father. It is not that a crippled man can't be a good father, but an angry man can't. Jesus changed his heart and hence our whole family. It's not that we didn't love each other before, but now we have a way and a reason to show it. Jesus Christ is still alive and well and we are the living proof."

Rebekah, Aeneas' wife, could say very little through the joyful tears and laughter. But her eyes danced as she baked the daily bread, and she did manage to say this, "Our gracious Lord, Jesus Christ has given me back my husband, friend and lover. We will no longer be poor, but we will always be his slaves."

Meanwhile, some fourteen miles away in Joppa, the ladies group of the local synagogue gathered mournfully at the bedside of their matron leader, Dorcas Tabitha. As she neared death's door the rumor of Aeneas reached their city. They sent Aristarchus and Archaelaus, fleet-footed messengers, to sequester the miracle worker from Lydda. Unfortunately, it was too late. The veteran minister of benevolence died.

When Peter arrived, her body had already been washed and was prepared for anointing and wrapping. As Peter entered the room, he was accosted by the elderly women of the synagogue, displaying the shawls and blankets Dorcas had woven for the poor among their people. It was a touching scene filled with tears and tales. Eyewitnesses said that Peter offended many of them when he sent them out of the room. "What right does he have? Who does he think he is?" they asked.

One reliable inside source says that Peter then got down on his knees and prayed. He then turned to the corpse and said, "Tabitha, get up." These words are strikingly similar to those once used by Jesus of Nazareth when he purportedly raised a twelve year old girl by saying: "*Talitha* [little girl], get up."

Not much is known about what actually took place inside the room. But moments later out came Peter, arm in arm with Tabitha. One of the widows there had this to say, "It is the greatest miracle of God. In the name of Jesus Christ, the dead are raised! What else can we do but become Christians?"

Local lore and rumors are running wild. Some say she was merely resuscitated. Others are fully convinced that God healed her through Jesus. You can hear their story at the newly founded "First Christian Church of Joppa." Or if you want to go straight to the source, Simon Peter is now living with Simon the Tanner on the outskirts of the city.

Whatever these strange occurrences mean, this much is certain; the whole Plain of Sharon is abuzz with excitement and even some resentment. The Church of Jesus Christ is now firmly entrenched in our towns. For better or worse, Jesus is still making a difference and is still touching lives in our villages.

My Witnesses

April 19, A.D. 57

Dr. Luke,

It was good to meet you yesterday in church. I do hope to meet Paul here in the near future. After all, it is only right that the Apostle to the Gentiles should meet the first Gentile convert. You know that I am now retired from active military duty. Nevertheless, I still have a substantial number of influential contacts under Felix's command. I'll see what I can do to pull some strings so as to ensure Paul's comfort and safety during his confinement. But just between you and me, I'm not overly optimistic. We have had more noble rulers than the present governor.

Well, on to the business at hand. You wanted my testimony, and I'm more than happy to give it. I served as a centurion in the Roman military. I led one hundred of the Empire's finest in the Imperial regiment. My life was most men's dream. I had a position of power and men who served me with dignity. I had a wonderful family and lived in a comfortable city with all the modern conveniences and diversions. But my heart was unsettled. Spiritually, I was searching.

Even as a Roman, Judaism always attracted me. My people had lost all faith in the Pantheon. Judaism's belief in one God was an attractive alternative. My culture had abandoned all moral absolutes. So naturally, the ethical standards of the Torah and the solid families of the synagogue were a welcome change. This says nothing of their benevolence, prayers, and education. I could go on, but you get the point. I loved Judaism as a religion. However, as a culture, I found it offensive. I mean, let's start with circumcision – the mutilation of the body, and such a cherished member at that! Then there were all the Jewish factions within, combined with its arrogance toward outsiders. They were so intolerant! This left me in "no man's land" in my search for God.

I adopted Jewish hours of prayer and a Jewish-style benevolence. These "good works," however, only made me hunger for

God more and still left me miserable in the guilt of my sin. Then one day it happened. About 3 p.m. I was praying, as usual. An angel of God came to me in a vision and told me about a guy named Simon Peter, living with Simon the Tanner in Joppa. I was shocked both at the vision and at its specificity. I mean, God even gave me the guy's address! Immediately I summoned three of my best men, one from the military and two from my personal household. I sent them to Joppa to bring this man to me. Luke, I can't tell you how my heart burned for the next four days. What if he refused to come? I knew how the Jews spurned Romans, especially the military peace-keeping forces. My only hope for the next seventy-two hours was my vague familiarity with the Jewish story of Jonah. He and Peter both started at Joppa, you know.

With my military background, I calculated the approximate length of the journey and its return. I prepared my family and friends for Simon Peter's arrival. Four days later, to the hour, all the acquaintances I could summon were assembled in my house. Could this be the moment I had been waiting for? Could this Jew tell me how to come to the Living God? Luke, I don't know your biography or how you came to Jesus, but as a Gentile, perhaps you can share the anxiety and joy of my testimony.

When I saw them coming, my heart skipped a couple of beats I can tell you. I ran out to Peter and bowed at his feet as I would before any notable general. He seemed uncomfortable with such homage, even a bit put off. Great! The first thing I do in a potentially volatile racial situation is offend the sensibility of my would-be preacher!

I was awed at the moment. God had just broken the ethnic bounds of his chosen people. Later I would find out that this was prophesied in the Bible. But none of the Jews seemed to see it, or if they did they hid it well! Peter was as taken by the moment as I. In fact, he opened his sermon by saying, "You all know what a risk I'm taking here. It is against our traditions to associate with foreigners, let alone enter your homes!" Peter wasn't telling us anything we didn't already know. We always thought the Jews were ignorant bigots and didn't much miss their fellowship. Nevertheless, we did appreciate Peter's generous gesture.

Nothing else in Peter's sermon was radically new either. We had already heard about God the creator, John the Baptist and even Jesus of Nazareth. After all, none of these things were done in a corner. It was not even a surprise that Peter said, "I now realize how true it is that God does not show favoritism." It seemed shocking to him that we were acceptable to God, but we all had realized our own humanity long before.

So, there were no great surprises *until* Peter got to the end of his sermon. When he claimed that Jesus was risen from the dead, that was news to me. Oddly, I believed it. Why shouldn't I? I knew God was real; he gave me this vision. I believed in his power to create life, why not his power to renew it? Peter was a credible witness according to every rule of jurisprudence I knew. He himself claimed to be an eyewitness to the bodily resurrection of Jesus. I had no reason to doubt, so I didn't.

Then came the real bombshell: Jesus' death and resurrection secured our forgiveness of sins. **That's what I had been looking for!** Eureka! In my heart I believed. That started a chain reaction. First, God granted me faith to believe, and I ran with it! Next, all my natural reserve went right out the window. I began to praise God uncontrollably and unfettered. My family and friends followed suit. Then the Holy Spirit came down upon us. The physical sensation was wonderful but irrelevant. The important thing is that we began speaking fluently in languages we had never studied. All we knew was that we had been touched by God. But apparently to Peter and his six Kosher companions this was a sign from God that we were acceptable candidates for membership in the church.

Peter was tongue-tied. (From what I gather, that didn't happen to him very often). Come to think of it, I don't believe Simon ever finished his sermon. He simply said, "Uh . . . Uh . . . Uhhhh . . . Can any of you guys think of a reason not to immerse these people into the body of Christ?" No one said a word, so they did. Peter stayed for a few days before leaving us under the tutelage of Philip the Evangelist. He and I have served the church together here for the better part of 20 years. Sure, we still have our cultural differences and preferences, and I won't kid ya, they sometimes still cause tension. But Luke, in these days of racial strife, we need to preach Christ as the balm for the nations. Ethnic tension will never be healed until all men are committed to something greater than themselves. Jesus is the only figure that looms large enough over us all unto which all men can be drawn. As the first Gentile convert, it is my prayer that the church will be colorful precisely because she is color-blind.

For the love of Christ and his Bride,

Cornelius

AN INVESTIGATIVE REPORT

Subject: Gentile Inclusion – can Gentiles become Christians without first becoming Jews?

Occasion: The Apostle Peter baptized the household of Cornelius prior to their conversion to Judaism. This action was unauthorized by the Jerusalem Elders. This investigative report will determine whether Peter's actions were acceptable or not, and ultimately whether Cornelius and his family should be considered Christian brothers.

Sponsors: The Judaizers, converted Pharisees who serve with James, the brother of the Lord Jesus Christ and Elder at Jerusalem.

PART A – Simon Peter's Testimony

After the healings of Aeneas in Lydda and Dorcas in Joppa, I settled in the house of one Simon the Tanner. One morning I went up to the roof-top to pray. Brunch was about an hour late and I thought a time of meditation would take my mind off food. Boy was I wrong! I had a vision of a large sheet with all kinds of animals on it, many of them were unclean (pigs, lobsters, rabbits, etc.). In my vision, the Lord commanded me to get up, kill and eat. I thought it was a test. With a sense of Jewish pride I refused. "Lord," I said, "You know my lips are clean and will ever remain so!" But a second time he told me to kill and eat. I refused. Then a third time he gave this same command. Again I refused. (I'm beginning to think that three is not such a lucky number for me!).

The Lord said, "Peter, stop calling unclean what I have declared clean!" Suddenly I realized that God wasn't kidding. Moreover, I realized that God was talking about people, not food. But what on earth was I supposed to do about it? I sat and stewed over the vision (pardon the pun).

I would not have to wait long to find out God's intention. Talk about impeccable timing! At that very moment there was a knock at the door. Three Gentiles arrived and asked for me by name. Ok, so I may be hard-headed (they don't call me "Rock" for nothing, you know), but even I can recognize the guidance of God when it is this clear. These three fellows apparently didn't know what God had been doing with me, just as I had no idea what God had been doing with Cornelius. They tried to talk me into going with them. But that issue had already been settled. You see, when I heard the knock at the door, the Spirit told me in plain Hebrew, "Peter, three men are at the door asking for you because I have sent them here. Go downstairs and introduce yourself."

What could I do? I've learned that it's not such a good idea to argue with God. Even so, I must confess that I was more than a little uncomfortable. All my life I've been taught that these people are dirty. As we traveled and ate together, I found out that our similarities were more than our differences. They too love their families, long for God, laugh, cry, and bleed. They too have hopes and dreams, fears and preferences. There is nothing like living with someone to discover their full humanity!

To make a long story short, we left the next morning and arrived early on the second day. It was every preacher's dream. The crowd was already assembled and eager to listen. Right in the middle of my sermon the Holy Spirit interrupted. No kidding, these Gentiles were baptized with the Holy Spirit just as we were on Pentecost! They spoke in tongues just as we had. God's seal of approval was too obvious to ignore. What was I to do? Call unclean what God declared clean? You fellas do what you need to, but I am going to obey God rather than men!

PART B – Testimony of Simon the Tanner

Gentlemen, surely you are aware that Gentile inclusion into the church has been God's desire for a very long time. Did not Isaiah prophesy in 49:6, "It is too small a thing for you alone to serve me"? Does he not say in Isaiah 2 that all nations will stream to Mt. Zion? Did God not promise to our father Abraham that his seed would bless the *whole earth*? Wake up and smell the Rose of Sharon! The blood of Jesus Christ is for all people.

Can you not see God's preparation for this moment? The church of Jerusalem wrestled with racism over the Hellenistic widows. Then again a delegation was sent to Samaria to check out that "half-breed" church. Do you think it was an accident that Peter found a home at my place – a Jew with an "unclean" job?! Gentlemen, I know what it is like to be ostracized because of class and "cleanness". I have born the brunt of religious hypocrisy and hostility all my life. It must stop here! It must stop now!

Of course I was uneasy about having Gentiles stay in my house overnight. Of course our conversation was strained around the dinner table. What do you expect? Crossing bridges is dangerous and uncomfortable, but there is no other path to the great commission. "Going" demands crossing. We cannot obey Jesus and be a light to the world or be a witness to the ends of the earth without settling this issue. I'm not naive. I'm relatively certain that this issue of racism will rear its ugly head again. But I am ready to crush it with brutality again and again. If we don't, we will consign ourselves to being a small, friendly church that is comfortably homogenous, yet powerless, irrelevant, and viciously antagonistic to the will of God.

PART C:

Gentlemen, these six witnesses have corroborated Peter's story. Do we really have anything left to decide? This is clearly not Peter's scheme. Indeed, the Lord Jesus Christ has given him the keys to the Kingdom. He unlocked it for the Jews at Pentecost, the Samaritans by laying on his hands, and now to the Gentiles through a second Pentecost. In fact, we now see that John the Baptist's prediction has come true: Jesus baptizes all people with his Holy Spirit. Who do we think we are that we could oppose God?! We conclude, therefore, that Peter's actions are neither untrue to Judaism, nor to the prophets, but they fulfill God's plan for the nations.

We conclude that Judaism is the means through which Jesus was revealed as the Christ, but not the means through which

Gentiles must come to God. Faith in Jesus alone is sufficient to save, not obedience to Jewish regulations and traditions.

We conclude that God has even granted the Gentiles repentance which leads to eternal life. Blessed be the God of our fathers, the God of all nations, tongues and tribes.

My Witnesses

Brother Luke,

In response to your inquiry about the beginnings of the church at Antioch, all I can say is you would have **loved** it! It was a great ride on the wave of the Holy Spirit. When your good buddy Saul beat the stuffing out of the church in Jerusalem, we Hellenistic Jews found ourselves fugitives in foreign lands. Most of us wound up in places like Phoenecia, Cyprus and Antioch.

As you know, when seed is scattered, it grows. Christian churches began to pop up all over the place! I bet Saul kicked himself a hundred times for the way he kicked us to the four winds. I can just hear him say to the Sanhedrin: "Oops." The only problem was that these churches were merely transplanted Christian synagogues. They were not being faithful to the great commission of Jesus to make disciples of ALL nations. Further-more, they were not being faithful to the communities in which they found themselves. They practiced "selective" evangelism, telling the good news only to other Jews who looked, thought and acted like them. Their board meetings ran better, and they didn't offend the "sensibilities" of the Jerusalem church, but they broke the heart of God and forfeited influence in the community.

There was another group of us in Antioch, however, that began telling the good news to everyone. When we made a business deal, we would work Jesus into the conversation. When our landlords asked us what brought us to the area, we told them. When our wives went shopping and our children went to play in the park, we kept inviting people to Jesus.

I probably need to clarify a couple of things here. First, there was no "plan of attack." We weren't attacking anyone or even trying to build a church. Jesus just exuded from our conversations because he so filled our hearts. Second, we were not social activists trying to make a point or meet a quota. Evangelizing someone because of the color of their skin is nearly as offensive as NOT evangelizing someone because of the color of their skin. We were simply being a light where God placed our candlestick. Before long our church began to look a lot like our community.

We never considered the theological implications of multi-ethnic evangelism. We were just doing what came naturally. But believe me, the theological implications were thick, thick enough, in fact, to rock the church at Jerusalem. Before long they sent Barnabas. Some, I'm sure, intended for Barnabas to "check us out." Others simply wanted him to encourage us. I think you know Barnabas well enough to know which side of the fence he was on.

His encouragement and approval shook loose the vestiges of doubt among our own members and then our church took off like a rocket! With his spirit-filled leadership and love we grew beyond our ability to handle it. That's when Barnabas took off to Tarsus to hunt up Saul. It was no easy task either. Between Saul's church planting and ducking would-be assassins, he was hard to locate.

Finally, the two of them returned and it seemed like the church grew every day! This went on for the better part of a year. We made an indelible impact on Antioch. In fact, we almost made too much of an impact. Those that didn't join the church were far from apathetic towards us. With no middle-ground, the unbelievers opposed us and often verbally abused us. Get this, they coined a name for us. They had to, really, in order to differentiate us from the Jewish synagogues with whom they comfortably coexisted. They called us "Little Christs," as if that were an insult! That's where the term "Christians" originated. I don't think it would have stuck if we didn't consider it such a compliment. It was almost as if God gave the pagans a name to call us that both parties would enjoy.

More reinforcements arrived from Jerusalem. They even sent prophets to help the movement. It felt like the hand of God was moving from Jerusalem up to us to relocate the center of Christianity. During this time, one of the prophets named Agabus predicted a severe famine. (You remember the big one under Claudius?!) This was, of course, devastating. Yet for us, it was a wonderful opportunity to wed the two primary churches. Since the Jewish church gave Antioch the life-saving meat of the gospel, it was only right for the Gentile church to send life-saving funds to our brothers in Jerusalem. Each member gave every extra denarius (s)he could manage. What a joyous celebration we had when we sent it to the brothers through Barnabas and Saul. With tears in our eyes we imagined the tears in theirs when they would receive it. The beauty of the moment was not benevolence, but unity. Through this gesture the two movements were inextricably bound as one.

All in One and One in All,

Lucius of Cyrene

PSALM OF MARY
(On the occasion of the death of James and the release of Peter)

Wicked men spawn wicked sons,
    Adding evil deeds to evil.
Herod "The Great" pursued the Christ,
    So his son beheaded the Baptist.
Antipas arraigned the Passover Lamb,
    So his nephew beheaded the fisherman.
On and on the saga is sung,
    Until the righteous are vindicated
    and evil undone.

James embraced the steely death,
    the gates of Hades and Heaven's rest.
(O valiant martyr, first of the Twelve,
    Greet blessed Steven, leader of the white-robed band.)
The Jews rejoiced to taste his blood,
    and clamored for more of Herod's cruel feast.
When he who held the keys was captured,
    The church staggered in disbelief.
O bride of Christ, who besmeared your eyes?
    Who blurred your vision of the groom?
So soon you've forgotten his angelic release,
    So soon you succumb to disbelief.
Like Israel in the desert,
    You too quickly abandon your manna.

When Passover ended so would Peter's life,
    Justice is vanquished while religious scruples thrive.
The church was paralyzed but for one night of prayer.
    She gathered in the shadows, shrouded in despair.
Meanwhile, God is not silent,
    In spite of faithless disciples.
Peter rested that night in the grace of God,
    Ready to drink full from Jesus' own cup.

My Witnesses

As the last grains drained from the hourglass of execution,
    God's angel of stealth made mockery of prison bars.
The chilly passage and cold guards seemed but a dream.
    Yet a slap from the evening breeze awoke the Rock to
    reality.

Peter moved through the night like a phantom,
    was received at the door as a ghost.
A Rose yet to bloom, burst in the room,
    "It's Peter," she cried, "Our prayers reached the throne."
Our vigil ended; the debate began.
    We believed in his ghost more than God's grace,
    More than angels of mercy, or Abba's strong arm.
God opened the prison,
    But we had to open the door – to Peter . . . to the Lord.

Lord forgive us our faithless prayer,
    Forgive us our doubts and needless despair.
Grant us faith to believe and power to receive,
    Good gifts from the Groom, our God.

We celebrate your power to release the captives,
    From prisons of steel and of sin.
You heal and protect, reveal and provide,
    For your bride, the Church of the Living God.
We pledge you our praise, we promise our trust,
    For you have been faithful to your people at night,
    and led us again to hope in the Light.

AN HISTORICAL ANNOTATION FROM JOSEPHUS'
ANTIQUITIES XIX.8.2
(A rough draft, presented at the Society of Religious History
annual meeting, A.D. 59)

Now, after Agrippa had reigned for three years over all
Judea, he went to Caesarea (which used to be called Strato's
Tower). There he put on an exhibition in honor of Caesar after
he learned that these people held a festival in order to pray for his
safety. This festival attracted many important people from all over
the province. On the second day, Herod wore a cloak which was
woven from sterling silver. It was awesome! When he walked into
the theater that morning, the sun struck the garment and
produced a dazzling display. The crowd was astounded, even
mesmerized. Some began to cry out, "He is a god!" Others echoed
it back. Soon the whole place was chanting (though not for
Herod's good): "Be merciful to us; for up to now we reverenced
you only as a man, from here on out we will acclaim you as
supernatural." The king didn't quiet the crowd but let them
blaspheme.

Suddenly, he looked up and saw an owl sitting on a rope
above his head. Instantly he recognized the bird as a harbinger of
doom, just as it had once been a sign of good news.[1] Immediately
he became sorrowful. Just as quickly a severe pain arose in his
abdomen — an agonizing, burning pain. At this he looked at his
friends and said, "You call me a god, but I am about to die.
Providence reproves your lying lips. This 'immortal' is about to
taste death. What can I do but submit to Fate as God wills? I may
die poorly, but I have lived well, in luxury and splendor."

As soon as he said this his pain became violent. His
bodyguards whisked him away into the palace. Rumor quickly

---

[1]As prophesied, the first time Herod saw this owl he was released from
prison [*Antiquities* XVIII.6.7]. He was told that the second time he saw
this owl would be the day of his death.

spread that Herod was on his deathbed. His Jewish citizens, as was their custom, dressed in sackcloth and ashes and prayed to God for Herod's recovery. People were lamenting and crying everywhere. The king looked out his bedroom window and saw people laying on the ground crying for him, and he himself couldn't help crying for them.

After five days, the pain in his stomach wore him down, and he died. He was forty-five years old at the time. He had reigned for seven years, four years under Caius Caesar and three over Philip's tetrarchy as the sole administrator, and in his last year Herod's territory was added to his own. He also reigned for three years under Claudius Caesar, during which time he reigned over the aforementioned countries and also Judea, Samaria and Caesarea. The revenues he received from these countries was huge, more than twelve million drachmae.[2] Nevertheless, he still had to borrow a bunch of money, because he spent much more than he collected, much of it on gifts and parties for friends.

---

[2] A drachmae is a day's wage.

BOARD MEETING MINUTES
March 26, A.D. 45

Present: Barnabas (Joseph) of Cyprus, Simeon (Niger), Lucius of Cyrene, Manaen (friend of the Tetrarch), Saul of Tarsus.

7:00 p.m. Opened with prayer.

10:25 p.m. Old Business:

(1) Barnabas wondered if they needed to send more funds to the poor in Jerusalem. The issue was tabled until Agabus could be contacted for specific needs. It was unanimously agreed, however, that the church should meet any and all needs that arose.

(2) Manaen asked for a report from building and grounds. There didn't seem to be anything to report.

(3) Lucius gave a financial report. It appears that every last dime has been spent on feeding widows and orphans. All rejoiced that there was no surplus rotting in some account.

(4) Simeon expressed gratitude that there was no segregated seating at the Fellowship Dinners/Communion services. Barnabas confessed that there were still some Jews who were working through a bit of discomfort but all were enjoying the shrimp cocktail.

10:29 p.m. New Business:

(1) Simeon made a motion that Barnabas and Saul be payed for their services in teaching and preaching. It was seconded by Manaen. After a lively debate, Saul adamantly refused. He said something about preferring to make tents than rob God's people. The vote was 3 for, 2 against, which falls short of the 65% needed to carry the motion. It was denied.

(2)   Lucius brought up the issue of ordering new Sunday School curriculum. It was unanimously decided to simply use the Scriptures, in particular, the Old Testament.

(3)   All five Elders clearly heard a message from the Holy Spirit during a period of prayer, service and fasting. He said, "Set apart for me Barnabas and Saul for the work to which I have called them." Since this communique from the Holy Spirit was deemed an oracle of God, we decided to dispense with "Rabbi's Rules of Order," and act upon this motion without putting it to a vote. We will respond in the following ways:

    (a)   We will pray and fast for an extended period, seeking specific direction for the missionary team.

    (b)   We will have an ordination service where we lay our hands on the pair, pledging to them our prayers, financial support, and bestowing on them our own spiritual authority. They will be apostles from Antioch to plant new churches. They will become accountable to our leadership and report back to us the victories of God.

    (c)   We have assigned Manaen the task of explaining to the congregation why we are sending out our two best teachers to a missionary venture rather than social misfits with better than average language skills. We have asked him to communicate to our people that we tried to argue with the Holy Spirit on this point but he was characteristically persistent.

    (d)   We will book passage for the two to go to Cyprus, Barnabas' home. In our strategy session we decided that since Barnabas was familiar with the territory and culture, that would be a good place to begin to make inroads for the Gospel. From there, they will look to the north, territory which Saul is more familiar with. Since these areas all speak Greek, language training will not be necessary at this time. We have insisted, however, that Saul give up his part-time business for the time being, since this new work will demand his utmost attention. We have agreed to send sufficient funds so he would not have to take up collections from the newly planted churches. He graciously agreed.

11:05 p.m. Meeting adjourned.

OFFICIAL MEMO :
FROM THE OFFICE OF THE PROCONSUL

Date: May 3, A.D. 45
From: Sergius Paulus
To: Elymas Bar Jesus
RE: Termination of employment

I am aware that you will be unable to read this yourself for an indeterminate period of time. Nevertheless, you are being terminated for breach of contract, effective immediately, without severance pay. You are to have your desk cleared by Monday morning and return all state properties including office equipment, signet rings and keys.

Explanation: When I learned that you were hosting some "so called" soothsayers from the synagogues of Salamis, I wanted to hear them myself. As my spiritual/social advisor, I was paying you for just such contacts and information. Yet you did your best to keep us apart. That was my first clue that you were a fraud. Then, when I did get to hear them, you did your best to contradict their message. I must confess, I was surprised myself at how quickly I accepted their gospel. But it made so much sense. When they talked about the emptiness of idols and magic I was forced to admit that a child with a pair of dice could predict the future as well as you had been doing for me.

I was even more shocked at your response, however. When you saw your lucrative scam unraveling at the edges, you threw a fit. You called them liars, lunatics, charlatans – everything but hog farmers! I could see, however, that they weren't lying, nor were they insane, nor were they out for financial gain. In fact, even when I offered them a job, they refused.

I'm disappointed in you Bar-Jesus. I thought you were a friend. I thought you cared about my administration and the welfare of Cyprus. No, you merely cared about yourself. What's worse is that you were ready to sacrifice my eternal salvation for your own petty position and greed. You would have turned me from the living God so you could turn a buck.

Indeed, you almost did derail me from Christianity. It was Paul's miraculous intervention that convinced me. He saw through you more clearly than I. He was right when he called you Bar Satan instead of Bar Jesus. Indeed, you are a son of the Devil, bought by filthy lucre. When he struck you blind through the power of the Holy Spirit, it was then that my own eyes were opened.

I know you are a bitter man right now. Let me remind you, however, that my namesake inflicted this upon you with painful personal memories. He too spent a time in darkness, and it was precisely that which brought him to the light. If you will but repent and accept the Lord Jesus Christ, this "curse" will become an act of mercy. Furthermore, if you come to your senses and accept Jesus as the Lord of Light, I'm confident that there may yet be a place for you in my employment (obviously in a different capacity). Elymas, don't turn your back on your own Messiah. I am only grafted in, but you belong by birth.

Because I no longer need your services, and because of breech of contract, you are fired. But there is still time for you to escape the fire of hell. As your friend, I urge you to repent. None are so blind as those that will not see.

AN INTERVIEW WITH PAUL

Luke: I want to talk about your first evangelistic tour with Barnabas. But first, I have to ask you why you changed your name from Saul to Paul on this trip.

Paul: My Roman cognomen has always been Paul.

Luke: I understand that, but why does everyone in Jerusalem call you Saul, and everyone on the field call you Paul?

Paul: It really started after the conversion of Sergius Paulus, my most famous convert up to that point. That was a powerful moment for me that opened up my ministry to non-Jews. It got me thinking – if I were to reach Gentiles then I ought to have a name they could relate to. Besides, it didn't hurt that "Paul" means "dwarfish." Its more than a description of this hooked-nose, bow-legged, bald guy. It serves as a constant reminder that I am nothing. No matter how "successful" I become, "He must increase and I must decrease."

Luke: Tell me, why did you take over leadership of the team after your name change, when you moved from Paphos to Perga?

Paul: Luke, I really don't like your terminology, "take over." It was partly this misconception of "power" that caused John Mark to leave.

Luke: Speaking of that, why did John Mark leave? Was he homesick? Frightened of robbers? Upset with your leadership? Was the tour taking longer than he wanted? What was the deal? And did you consider his abandonment apostasy?

Paul: I would really rather not talk about that. Suffice to say, John Mark and I have since been reconciled. He is like a son to me and is a valuable part of my ministry. I've learned since then that people can be salvaged through second chances. Besides, John Mark has since grown in wisdom, perseverance and consistency. Now, what were we talking about?

Luke: Your leadership of the team.

Paul: Oh, yeah. As I was saying, I didn't "take over" anything. Barnabas and I both simply did what we did best. It quickly became apparent that I was the more experienced speaker, he was the more adroit encourager, and John Mark, well he did a great job hauling our luggage, performing baptisms and working with the youth.

Luke: Well, let's get down to business. I've heard so much about your trip to Pisidian Antioch.

Paul: It was a trip! We went straight to the synagogue. That became our *modus operandi*. There we found a ready audience, lovers of God who were already familiar with the Scriptures. We not only met Jews there but Gentile proselytes who became a link to the broader community. As is Jewish custom, when the Synagogue ruler saw educated strangers he invited us to present the message of the day.

Luke: Some say your synagogue speech is your classic sermon to the Jews – a model, so to speak, of how to speak to Hebrews.

Paul: That's true. However, I must confess that most of it was plagiarized from two other sermons. I borrowed from Peter's Pentecost sermon his explanation of both Psalm 16:10 and 110:1, that is, evidence of Jesus' resurrection and Messiahship. And from Stephen, I borrowed the idea of a Jewish history lesson demonstrating that Jesus is the fulfillment of our ancestral history and hopes. There is not much original in my message. (I'll give you a copy of my old sermon outline when we're done here).

Luke: How did they respond?

Paul: About like I did the first time I heard Peter and Stephen preach these messages. I was duly impressed with their oratory skill and the power of the prophecies pointing to Jesus. Yet I was infuriated at the theological implications of what they said. I was enamored with the Jewish history and culture it contained, but offended by the suggestion that I must submit to Jesus as Lord. I was compelled by the evidence of Jesus' resurrection, but found it difficult to believe that his death atoned for my sins.

Luke: So, did they try to stone you like you did to . . . uh, I mean, were they antagonistic?

Paul: On the contrary, they actually invited us back the next week to tell them more (not that we hadn't told them enough already). Some of them were obviously stalling, others were truly interested. In fact, a good number of them followed us to our quarters and asked question after question. The gossip mills began to grind, and before long we were the talk of the town.

Luke: You must have been pumped!

Paul: We really were. However, it was not long lived. When we arrived at the synagogue the next Saturday, every seat in the house was taken. People lined the aisles so we could barely get to the pulpit. Crowds continued to come, and they stood outside the windows. It seemed like everyone in the town came out.

Luke: So what's wrong with that?

Paul: What's wrong is that they were mostly Gentiles. No offense Luke. You know my heart. But you also know Jewish custom. When they saw the Gentiles crowding in at the altar call, they became jealous and started to speak abusively towards us.

Luke: You're kidding! They didn't want more people to come to God?

Paul: Luke, Jews don't tend to think evangelistically. Let me put it this way: My people tend to be more interested in the purity of the participants than the size of the party. When they saw all the Gentiles respond to Christ, they didn't want that kind of association. It was then and there that I said, for the first time, "We had to speak the word of God to you first. Since you reject it and do not

	consider yourselves worthy of eternal life, we now turn to the Gentiles!"
Luke:	Ouch!
Paul:	You have no idea how difficult that was for me. I love Judaism. I am a Hebrew-speaking Hebrew, of the tribe of Benjamin, a Pharisee of the strictest tradition. Yet the word of God says, "I have made you a light for the Gentiles, that you may bring salvation to the ends of the earth." As painful as this is, it is my calling. Although, I do hope and pray that by bringing many Gentiles to Christ, I might make my own countrymen jealous, thereby causing them to return in droves to their ancestral hopes. The only thing that made this Jewish rejection palatable is the overwhelming joy of my new Gentile brothers.
Luke:	Did their initial excitement wane as the days went on?
Paul:	No way! The church reproduced like rabbits! The entire area was quickly permeated with the Gospel. That's when the trouble began.
Luke:	You mean physical persecution?
Paul:	Close. The Jews stirred up a bunch of rich, busybodied women whose husbands had clout. Through their incessant whining, their husbands caused all kinds of trouble for us. Before long, we got the boot and had to leave town.
Luke:	What did you do?
Paul:	What could we do? We left. But before we did, we shook out their dust from our cloaks, as Jesus suggested.
Luke:	What did you do that for?
Paul:	It's a Jewish thing. It means we don't want to be defiled even by the dust of your feet.
Luke:	Oh. . . How clever. Well, how did the baby Christians take it? Were they devastated?
Paul:	We thought they would be. But surprisingly they were filled with joy and with the Holy Spirit. It is humbling to think that we are not the caretakers of the disciples, but

the Holy Spirit can do in them what he has already done in us.

Luke: So you just left town. You left them alone to make a go of it on their own?

Paul: No. We left with them the Word and the Spirit. We sent to them letters of encouragement and lifted to God prayers on their behalf. And when we could, we returned to establish elders to lead the congregation. My experience as a church planter all these years has proven that the Word, the Spirit, encouragement, prayers and leaders is a firm enough foundation for any fledgling church.

Dr. Luke,

We had heard rumors of a couple of miracle working evangelists up in Iconium. You see, our local merchants supply more than our grocery baskets. Their travels to larger cities supply us with news and gossip from around the area. So we had heard about Paul and Barnabas, but we never imagined that they would come to our little town.

I remember it well. I was in the market when I heard a ruckus at the city gate. This short little Jewish man was yammering on for any who would listen. Ok, so I was a bit curious myself. The sermon was only moderately interesting until he pulled the lame man into it. I can't say that I knew the guy personally. But ever since I was a little girl, he was a fixture at the city gate. He sat there looking forlorn and looking for a handout. Mid-sentence, Paul stopped, stared and said to lame beggar, "Stand to your feet!" It was ludicrous. The guy had been lame from birth. Obviously Paul was not aware of who this fellow was. You can imagine my shock when the lame man did as he was told. We all just kind of looked at each other, then squinted at the lame man to make sure it was him. Then we looked at each other again with our jaws on our chest.

We had never seen anything like it. We did have a story in our local lore, however, that suddenly came to life. We had always been taught the story of Bacus and Philemon. It was kind of a fun myth. It goes something like this. Once upon a time, Zeus and Hermes came to Lystra disguised as beggars. They went the length of the town asking for handouts but were rebuffed at each door. Finally, on the edge of town, they came to the house of Philemon and Bacus. They were a poor elderly couple who had nothing to spare but a pet goose. They were benevolent folks so they killed the goose, fed the beggars and put them up for the night. Sometime after midnight, Zeus and Hermes revealed themselves to the couple and ordered them out of the house for they were about to destroy the city. When they were a safe distance away, they brought fire from heaven and leveled the town. They then rebuilt Lystra at its present location, established a temple to Zeus and installed Philemon and Bacus, as priest and priestess. That was the story. Cute, huh?

Well, as you can imagine, when Saul performed this stunning miracle, our minds rehearsed the fable. We were instant converts to Greek mythology. We began to shout, "The gods have come down to us in human form!" We assumed that Paul was Hermes, the chief speaker, and that left Barnabas to be Zeus. The priests scurried out the gate, around the corner to the temple and sequestered a couple of the sacrificial oxen, decorated with wreaths.

All of this took several minutes. Barnabas and Paul stood dumbfounded. They had no idea what was about to happen. How could they? In our excitement we had reverted to our native Lycaonian dialect. There was a lot of shouting and confusion. When Paul finally saw the oxen and put the pieces of the puzzle together, he just threw a fit (as I'm sure you know that Paul can do)! He tore his clothes like a good Jew in a bad mood. That was as foreign to us as our language was to him. We still got the point, but we were not about to be dissuaded. Our people had neglected to worship Zeus and Hermes once. We were not about to make that same mistake again. Nonetheless, Paul persisted in his objections. He assured us that they were mere mortals and that God alone deserved such sacrifice. He had a hard time, but he finally convinced the priest to take the ox back to the barn . . . alive.

After that, it wasn't long before Barnabas and Paul had the church established. Being raised as a Jew, it was natural for me and my daughter, Lois, to become charter members of the church. After all, it is the predicted fulfillment of Judaism.

The founding church had barely gotten started when a group of disgruntled Jews came all the way from Antioch and Iconium to stir up trouble. Boy did they have a bee in their bonnet! I'm not exactly sure what their beef was. The only thing I can figure out is that they lost control of the synagogues in their cities because so many of their leaders and leading members joined the church. Could it be that they would travel over a hundred miles spurred on only by jealousy and lust for revenge?

They told the citizens of Lystra that Barnabas and Paul had caused riots in their cities and jeopardized their status as Roman cities. With surprising ease, they convinced the crowd that their miracle was wrought by the power of the devil, and not by the power of God. They claimed that these men were bad Jews and worse Romans, that they were outlaws and impostors deserving of death. Paul bore the brunt of the attack. Their failed plot in Iconium came to fruition in Lystra. They stoned him right inside the city. My fellow citizens didn't know what a violation this was, but I did. In our Jewish law it states that a man is to be stoned outside the city. As if to make up for their mistake, they dragged Paul's limp corpse out the gate and left him for dead.

I suppose that it was somewhat bold on our part to go tend to his body. But then again, our intention was to bury him honorably, not to harbor a fugitive. We were stunned as Paul gasped for breath. We were overjoyed that he was still alive. We had to be careful that our exuberance wasn't overheard. We waited until nightfall and then carried him back into the city and tended his wounds. Early the next morning we ushered the two of them off to Derbe, a town even smaller than ours, a place where they could stow away until the uproar had died down and the Jews returned to Antioch and Iconium.

I was sad that my grandson, little Timmy, had to see such a brutal attack at such a formative age. I was afraid that it would give him nightmares and possibly even scare him away from the church. Nevertheless, he seems to be faithful to Jesus in his own right, even against his father's influence to paganism. At the risk of sounding like a doting grandmother, I must tell you how proud I am of him. Please take care of Timothy. He is still young and impressionable and could use a couple of good male role models in his life.

Love,
Eunice

My Witnesses

November 9, A.D. 61

To: Luke
From: Gaius of Derbe

The first time I ever met Paul he was a mess. He stumbled into town with a crutch in one hand and Barnabas in the other. We knew by their appearance that they were either victims of highway bandits or fugitives of the law. Naturally, when we found out they were the latter, we were surprised that they were willing to talk about it. Paul, the one who had been bludgeoned pretty badly, seemed especially eager to tell his story. In fact, it almost sounded like he was bragging about being beaten for being a pestilence to his own people.

What is even more strange is that we so readily accepted his story. We were a small town and therefore easily entertained by the whole saga. But we were not gullible. In fact, we normally hold newcomers at arms-length. These two were different, however. They had an honesty and a genuineness that just radiated from them. We didn't merely accept their story, we bought into it, and a church was born. A considerable portion of our citizens joined the new Jesus band.

Things got going so fast and they were going so well. Just as quickly, it seems, Paul and Barnabas said that it was time for them to go. We argued with them voraciously. But what could we do? They insisted on getting back to Antioch. Even our manliest men shed more than a few tears. It wasn't so much that we would miss Paul and Barnabas, although that was breaking our hearts. It was that we feared for the future of our congregation. Who would be our leaders? It's tough to replace a preacher like Paul, you know.

They taught us that when the people of God encountered difficult decisions and situations, the proper thing to do was to fast and pray. We did. Through this process, several men were chosen to be Shepherds of the flock and the two apostles of Antioch, Paul and Barnabas, laid their hands on their heads and prayed for them. They thus delegated their authority, the authority of Christ, via the church at Antioch, to these men who would be our leaders. They left us with these words: "We must go through many hardships to enter the kingdom of God." I'll tell you, those words had great impact coming from Paul whose scars and bruises were still painfully plain.

As they began to leave, we thought they had gotten turned around. They were going the wrong direction. They headed Northwest, but Antioch, as well as Paul's hometown of Tarsus, was Southeast. We said, "Hey fellas, Antioch is the other way." "Yes," they said, "But we must return to Lystra, Iconium and Psidian Antioch to install Elders for their churches just as we did for yours." I could hardly believe my ears! "Why don't ya just gird up your loins, stand under a hornets nest and beat it with a stick! Are you crazy? Those guys are gonna beat the tar out of you, Paul!" Again we tried to argue with them. But those two are as stubborn as a Pharisaic donkey on the Sabbath. Their concern for the churches took precedent over their personal welfare.

We were worried sick over them. Yet God was gracious and answered our prayers for their safety. They retraced their steps and established badly needed leaders in these foundling churches. They did skip the churches of Cyprus, likely since they didn't face the same kind of persecution as the brothers in Asia Minor. Besides, there were already Christians on Cyprus long before Paul and Barnabas got there. They would be able to provide the leadership these folks needed to survive and thrive.

I can only imagine the joyous reunion they had back in Antioch, their sending church. My, the stories they must have told, the hugs, the tears, the thanks given to God. I didn't know if I would ever see Paul again. But God was gracious and allowed me not only to see him but participate with you guys in ministry. Our traveling days were never dull, our conversations never mundane. I envy you, my friend, to be with Paul, even when he is in chains.

My Witnesses

Dear Luke,

Thanks to me, you didn't have to go through out-patient surgery to become a Christian! Here's the story. I was a member of the church at Antioch. Some right-wing legalists came up from Jerusalem claiming to be from James, Jesus' brother. They looked me straight in the eye and said that I was not a Christian and therefore was going to hell. Why? Because I had not mutilated my flesh by cutting off my foreskin. At first I thought they were kidding. But no, they were serious.

They explained that the Jews alone were God's people and that only God's people could come to Christ. As you can imagine, I was at a loss for words. I was not a trained theologian. All I knew was that Jesus died for my sins and I loved him. They had the gall to tell me that wasn't enough! They said the cross of Christ was an addition to the law, not a substitute for it.

You should have been there. Paul threw a fit! (I know, that's hard to believe.) He said, "You bunch of legalistic, pharisaical hypocrites . . . and I would know one because I used to be one! We are not saved by circumcision or any other work of the law. We are saved by the work of Christ alone. In fact, if you try to add circumcision to the cross, you'll be severed from Christ, you'll fall from grace. Mark my words: You'll be damned."

Well, our church was pretty shaken up. We wanted to believe Paul. But what if these guys were right? After all, they were from Jerusalem, from James the Elder! Paul and Barnabas said, "Look guys, we'll go down to Jerusalem ourselves and get this thing straightened out." So off they went. They invited me to go along. I agreed. But while I was packing my bags I realized that I was not a spectator, I was a test case. Yikes!

Paul and Barnabas were so sure that they were right that on the way down to Jerusalem, they preached in Phoenicia and Samaria how the Gentiles had been converted. Talk about *chutzpa*! Once we arrived in Jerusalem, we had a private meeting with the church leaders and Apostles. Paul told them about all the Gentile converts. They rejoiced as much as the brothers in

Phoenicia and Samaria at God's grace. These yahoos "from James" didn't have a chance at the council, the deck was already stacked against them (not to mention truth).

When the council convened, the Judaizers were up first. It was the same old rabble about respect for God's law. You know, Jesus said, "I've not come to destroy the law but to fulfill it – not a jot or tittle will pass away." They yammered on about how we need the law to ensure righteousness. They talked about how they were the natural olive tree and we were to be grafted in.

After they sat down, Peter got up. It was beautiful! He said, "Look here, I got the keys! By God's design I unlocked the door to the Jewish Church on Pentecost and to the Gentile Church at Cornelius' house. It wasn't my idea to accept the Gentiles, it was God's. The Holy Spirit put his stamp of approval on them with the gift of tongues. God commanded us to stop calling unclean what he accepts as clean. You try to put a yoke on their necks that you haven't been able to carry. Now cut it out and quit trying to cut them off! We were saved by the grace of Jesus, they are saved by the grace of Jesus. There is no difference between us."

What was left to say? According to Paul and Barnabas, plenty! They both got up and spoke. I'll spare you all the details. You can read a synopsis of their sentiments in the letter Paul wrote to the churches of Galatia. The upshot was that the law was a tutor which led us to Christ but after that was powerless for either salvation or righteousness. Think about this last line, it is packed with power and truth. The audience sat spell-bound as they listened to story after story of Gentiles transformed by the power of God. Then he pointed at me as one last example. Talk about uncomfortable. All eyes were one me. I held my breath as Paul said, "Are you telling me that we need to circumcise Titus?!"

Boy was I relieved when James broke the tension of the moment. He stood and said, "We're not gonna cut anyone here today." That was music to my ears. But it was not nearly as beautiful as the passage he quoted from Amos 9:11-12, "After this I will return and rebuild David's fallen tent. Its ruins I will rebuild, and I will restore it, that the remnant of men may seek the Lord, and all the Gentiles who bear my name, says the Lord, who does these things that have been known for ages." For the first time, I saw myself in the Bible. I had a place in David's tent – I belonged to the household of faith. God loved me and invited me into his kingdom. I already knew I was a member in good standing with Paul and Barnabas. But now I saw that I was adopted into God's family and a central player in the kingdom. Luke, do you know what this means? We're in . . . **we're in!!!**

Obviously it is not a simple task to unify two cultures. It may sound attractive to say, "We simply need to love each other and accept our differences," but it is also naive to expect that to happen. James was wise to write this letter ordering the Gentiles to abandon all vestiges of idolatry, including meats sacrificed to idols, strangled animals, blood and sexual immorality. Please understand. James was NOT writing a Gentile version of the ten commandments. These were not laws but essential ordinances for Christian unity between Jews and Gentiles. Moses' teachings were so proliferated all over the empire that if we showed even a hint of idolatry in the church it would likely split. So we rejoiced to keep these rules in order to preserve the unity of the church. We kept them, not in order to be saved but because we were. We kept them because, as recipients of Christ's grace, we were compelled to graciousness with our Jewish brothers.

Now, my friend, here is our most difficult task. We must show the same acceptance and openness to the Judaizers that the Apostles have shown to us. It would do no good for us to be grafted in, only to cut off the natural branches who tried to cut us off. Anyone with his nose bent out of shape in the church needs to take another look at the contorted body of Christ on the cross. We must pray with the Master, "Father, forgive them, for they know not what they do."

Wholly His,

Titus

AN OPEN LETTER

June 30, A.D. 50

From:	The Apostles of Jesus, the Elders at Jerusalem, and your Jewish brothers in Christ
To:	The churches of Antioch, Syria and Cilicia
RE:	The Jewish legalists and Gentile inclusion

Our Dear Brothers:

It has come to our attention that some Judaizers came to Antioch claiming to have come with my blessing, James, the half-brother of Jesus of Nazareth. We understand that they created quite a stir, disturbing your churches. Please be assured that they do *not* speak for us and do *not* have our blessing or authority. For this reason the leadership here in Jerusalem has decided on the following course of action.

(1) We affirm our love and admiration for our dear friends, Barnabas and Paul. These brothers have risked their lives for the Lord Jesus Christ. They deserve your respect and attention.

(2) We have commissioned Judas and Silas to confirm in person what we are writing. They will testify to our support of Barnabas and Saul and our decision *not* to require circumcision of Gentile Christians.

(3) The only requirements we would place upon the Gentiles, according to the guidance of the Holy Spirit, are these four: That they avoid foods sacrificed to idols, blood, meat of strangled animals, and sexual immorality.

If you abide by these four rules your churches will thrive.

Sincerely,

James & Co.

ADDENDUM: AN OPEN LETTER FROM JUDAS

November 1, A.D. 50

To: The Brothers in Syria and Cilicia

Silas and I were commissioned by the leaders in Jerusalem and by the Holy Spirit to accompany Barnabas and Paul back to Antioch to confirm the Gospel of Grace. We affirm, as prophets of God, the orthodoxy of these two men. Those Judaizers who accused them are *not* from James. They are imposters and legalists. We are in a position to know since we *are* from James. We were there at the Jerusalem council and can assure you that to a man the leadership sided with Paul. The Judaizers were rebuked and strictly warned not to spread their heresy of "works righteousness" any further. Nor are they to speak against God's chosen vessels again, at the risk of the wrath of God and the discipline of the church.

When we arrived in Antioch, this message was received with enthusiasm by the brothers. We all celebrated the grace of Christ and our freedom in him. We urge you to follow suit. I've stayed in Antioch a considerable time and watched the church continue to grow in good works, converts and unity. They are a model you can follow.

There are duties in Jerusalem which now demand my attention. Therefore, I write this letter to accompany Silas' personal testimony. For the time being, Silas will remain in Antioch. Should the Holy Spirit call Barnabas and Saul to return to your territory, Silas may, in fact, accompany them and confirm this message face to face.

The grace of our Lord be with your Spirit, Brethren, Amen.

January 1, A.D. 51

My heart is sick today, for I am reminded of my failure. It's been nearly a decade, but I still can't shake the shame of leaving Paul in Pamphylia. Even if I could forget it, he seems determined to remind me of it. Ever since I returned to Antioch to work alongside my cousin, Barnabas, Paul's countenance has declared his disappointment in me. Whenever our eyes meet, he looks away. His constant avoidance, his stiff posture, and his subtle allusions in his sermons to faithfulness under adverse situations all tell of his disdain for me. Even my direct apology had no apparent effect. But if there were ever a doubt about Paul's feelings for me, they were clarified today in front of everyone.

My heart stopped when I heard Barnabas' proposal. "It's time for another tour," he said. "Let's go back to the churches we planted and see how they're doing. Let's take John Mark with us. The brothers will want to see how he's grown just as we want to see how they've grown." You could almost hear Paul grind his teeth. He replied, "The tour is a good idea . . . taking John is a bad one! The stakes are too high, the travel too rigorous. He apostatized once; I'll not risk it again!" APOSTATIZED! So now the truth comes out. I knew he was angry, but I had no idea he considered me a heretic!

Barnabas caught it too and rose to my defense. "Paul, give it up man! You are making far too great a deal of his failure. He was young, it was his first real trip away from home. Even we did not know what to expect. Furthermore, it's been almost a decade since then and John has changed. He's proved himself faithful."

Barnabas was right. After leaving Pamphylia and returning to Jerusalem for a short stay, I followed Peter to Rome. There he hid from Herod's sword. He mentored me for several years. He was like a father to me, and I like a son to him. I heard him preach, I recorded his words. My work is now being published all over the empire. Many brothers have been encouraged by my book. I know I've outgrown my error; I know I'm a veteran worker for the kingdom. So why do I feel like such a failure? Because I still seek Paul's approval, which I may never get.

Paul argued that a delegate appointed by the church must be above reproach. "We just can't take a chance," he said. At that Barnabas came uncorked. "We can't take a chance?! We can't take a chance?!!! So you don't want to do for John what I did for you in Jerusalem?! Have you forgotten, 'Saul,' who it was that risked his life and reputation to introduce you to the Apostles? Have you forgotten who hunted you down to bring you to Antioch? You hypocrite! We're taking John Mark."

Paul had no more arguments but plenty more words. "We're *not* taking him on any trip I go on." "Fine!" Barnabas replied, "Then you can just stay here!"

The argument raged on; I hung my head in shame. I felt like an adulteress who broke up a happy marriage. Surely it was just a bad dream. They were an inseparable, unbeatable pair. They can't split up! I tried to back out but Barnabas wouldn't hear of it.

The Elders were speechless, the brothers dumbfounded and not a little bit frightened. Their primary leaders were going at each other and preparing to go their separate ways. They gave their support to Paul and Silas, but that doesn't mean they were on their side. They never censored me or Barnabas.

The only good thing about today is that there are now two teams. Although we couldn't work through our differences, we can at least work cooperatively. Barnabas and I agreed to visit the churches of Cyprus, where he grew up, while Paul and Silas headed off through Cilicia, Paul's home territory. This was significant for us. For while we couldn't maintain organizational unity because of our radically different ministry philosophies, none of us were about to abandon spiritual unity in Christ. We disagreed vehemently, yet our love remained intact. I'm sure the Lord was not honored by our argument. Yet I wonder if the Holy Spirit will be able to bring good from our separation and multiply our efforts. I pray to that end.

JOURNAL ENTRY #1: APRIL 10, A.D. 51

For the past 10 years, since I got out of med school, I have been working as a physician in Troas. It is a relatively small community on the eastern coast of the Aegean Sea. It is a pleasant life, with security, good pay, and predictable comfortability. Today, however, all that changes. At 2:30 p.m. I will set out for Macedonia with a team of three other evangelists.

Paul, a converted Hellenistic Pharisee, is at the helm. He is a veteran preacher, a pretty fair author, and a brilliant scholar of Scripture. What doors this doesn't open, his Roman citizenship will. Added to all his other talents is his extraordinary miracle-working power. Jesus himself trained Saul in Arabia, ordained him an Apostle and granted him supernatural abilities. Even I was overwhelmed by his intellectual prowess and his ability to heal. Naturally, he easily won me to Christ. Indeed, Paul is uniquely gifted to be the Apostle to the Gentiles.

The second member of the team is a Jerusalem Jew named Silas. His gift of prophecy and his participation in the Jerusalem council prepared him to augment Paul's preaching with both Jews and Greeks. His Roman citizenship may come in handy as well.

The third team member is Timothy, from Lystra. His youthfulness helps him relate to "Generation A" (for Adolescents). Furthermore, as a half-Greek, half-Jew, he has been especially helpful in racial reconciliation in some pretty bigoted areas. Since Paul circumcised him, he even has a voice in the synagogues with the other proselytes. He is such an outstanding young person that he had earned a reputation as a Godly man as far away as Iconium, a good two days journey from his home.

Obviously I add some medical expertise to the team. This is always an attraction for the gospel and an extension of Jesus' work as the great physician. Furthermore, as a born and bred Greek, there are some groups with which I alone will be able to initiate contact. As an aside, I also plan to keep a journal of our travels.

My Witnesses

This team is so well balanced. We all agree that it has been constructed by the sovereign hand of God. If there were ever any doubt that potential good could come from Paul and Barnabas' rift, this team should alleviate it. Furthermore, God escorted Paul and Co. right to my front door. He was touring Cilicia, Galatia and Phrygia, delivering the decree of the Apostles and elders in Jerusalem. They tried to turn south towards Asia, roughly retracing their steps from the first tour. The Holy Spirit, however, had different plans. Since they couldn't go south, they turned up toward Bithynia. Again they were hindered by Jesus. They had no other choice but to pass through the heart of Mysia, arriving here at Troas.

Where else was Paul to go? After making a few converts here (your's truly included), Paul was confused and not a little frustrated. What should be his next step? Then it happened. Last night he had a dream. There was a Macedonian man who begged Paul to come over and help them. I'll tell you what, those Macedonians are different. Historically, the Aegean Sea has kept us apart in more than one way. Their women are more liberated and their philosophers more elitist (I may enjoy them on both counts).

The four of us are beside ourselves with anticipation as we frantically pack and pray. I know not what this adventure holds, but I know it will be rich. God has prepared each of us all our lives for just such a time as this. Moreover, he has assembled us into a unified and highly tuned team. God has ordained our steps to the brink of Macedonia and we're ready to cross over and plant churches. It makes me wonder who God will raise up from among our converts, what waters they will cross in the future, and what churches will be born because of our present efforts.

A HISTORY OF THE 1ST CHRISTIAN CHURCH OF PHILIPPI
By Lydia and Zōn

It was the winter of 51 when a team of traveling evangelists showed up in Philippi. No one really paid too much attention when they arrived from Neapolis. We are, after all, a commercial crossroads and one of the leading cities of Macedonia. Strangers are not unusual to us. However, when they came to our prayer meeting down at the Gangites river, they stood out like a sore thumb. You see, Philippi is a Roman colony. We didn't have the ten Jewish men necessary to establish a synagogue in our city. So we met with a small group, mostly women, to pray to our God each Sabbath. Naturally, four educated Jewish men (well, two and a half of them were Jewish), caught our attention. We were delighted to have them teach. It was a rare treat to have a bonafide rabbi in our midst.

Trust me, I'm no gullible gal. I'm a business women of some prominence. I started my company in Thyatira and now do business in Philippi. In other words, I've been around the block a time or two. Furthermore, the trade I'm in (purple dye) is notorious for underhanded cheats. Therefore, I've become a pretty good judge of character. So my conversion was no small thing. As I listened to Paul, the Lord opened my heart and I believed in the Lord Jesus Christ. Immediately I put feet to my faith and was immersed into Jesus. My influence also caused the conversion of my employees and their families who were living in my house.

We urged the evangelists to stay with us. It would save them rent and provide us with the essential teaching we needed for discipleship. It took some talking, but I finally closed the sale. I can be a very persuasive person, you know.

Our church was small with a majority of females, but very committed and excited about what the Lord was doing. It wasn't all easy, however. For instance, one day as we were walking to the place of prayer, we were met by a slave girl. She was well-known in the city as the little fortune teller. Most people kind of felt sorry for her. Her owners made a lot of money off her. She was a mess because of the cultic practices and ritual drugs they subjected her to. Nevertheless, she did have an uncanny ability to predict the future. Well, she started tagging along behind us shouting, "These men are servants of the most high God! They are telling you a way you can be saved." This wasn't exactly the kind of publicity Paul was looking for. He wanted, in no way, to be associated with witchcraft and idolatry. Euodia and Syntyche debated about what to do with her. Nevertheless, Paul was very patient. He just put up with it. After a few days, however, he had all he could stand and he finally put an end to it. He wheeled around with a fire in his eyes. He spoke directly to the demon, "In the name of Jesus Christ I command you to come out of her!"

Just that quick the demon was gone. But so too was the owners' profit. I don't know what it's like where you live, but here in Philippi you can get away with any kind of pagan heresy or worldly indulgence, but don't you *dare* touch people's pocketbooks. We knew this was going to cause trouble, but we had no idea how much good God was going to bring out of it. Our church had three difficulties. (1) We were mostly women. Don't misunderstand, as the matron of this body and an independent business woman, I'm all for women's ministries. Nevertheless, we need to be realistic, without strong male leadership, we weren't going to make a significant impact on our community. (2) Because we were small, we needed to advertise a little bit better. We needed to attract the attention of a wider circle of people. (3) There was some question about the legality of a new sect like Christianity in this Roman colony. Within twenty four hours God would use this difficult circumstance to solve each of these problems. At this point I must turn it over to Zōn, the jailer, and let him finish the story.

I was the captain of the jail, so it didn't take long for me to hear about the hoopla. I got the whole scoop from my buddies on the Agora beat. They told me that when the owners of the slave-girl realized Paul "broke their toy" and robbed them of their little scam, they snatched him up along with his Jewish partner, Silas. The two were escorted to the marketplace and turned over to the police. The police stood them before the judge and accused them of instigating a riot and then promoting new and illegal religious practices. The crowds fell in like marionettes. They knew nothing about the charges but delighted in beating up a couple of Jews. They were an easy target since most Romans despise Jews for their arrogant ethnocentrism, anti-social self-righteousness and physical mutilation. They were beaten to a bloody pulp with billy clubs and handed over to me for safe keeping.

They were a mess. I wish I could say I felt sorry for them. But my line of work has a way of hardening a man. I slapped their hands in chains and their ankles in stocks. The wooden beams keep their legs spread apart so they can't stand up and run. They were shoved to the floor with their faces in the dust and their swollen, bloody backs against the dank evening air. Most men in my jail cursed me. These guys groaned a bit and grimaced in pain, but no foul words fell from their lips. I was impressed with how manly and dignified they were.

They were beaten pretty severely, and we provided nothing to dull the pain. We saved all the whiskey for ourselves. It was no surprise that they couldn't sleep. I was shocked to watch how they passed the time. You'll think I'm kidding, but this is the honest to God truth — they sang hymns and prayers to God. Usually the jail is filled with curses of God and fellow man, cries of pity and despair. Paul and Silas were so unusual, other-worldly . . . almost weird. There was a sacred hush as the other prisoners listened to this sweetness in the midst of the darkness. It was the only time my jail was ever a sanctuary.

Suddenly God accompanied them. He played percussion. An earthquake hit that was unbelievable. Philippi is on a fault line, so tremors are not unheard of. But this one shook the foundations and rattled open the doors of the cells. It somehow even unlocked the chains and shackles of the prisoners. I was shaken up, and yes, even shaken awake. I'm a bit embarrassed to admit it, but I was taking a little cat-nap. I guess their singing soothed me to sleep! Normally that would be no big deal. No one gets by my strong iron doors.

As I leaped to my feet and saw all the doors flung open, I drew my sword, not to keep the prisoners in but to kill myself. Let's be realistic for just a moment. One guard can't ward off all those prisoners. I would have been held responsible for their escape. All of their punishment would fall on *me*. As a Roman soldier, suicide was both honorable and easier than the fate that awaited me.

Paul must have seen my silhouette with a drawn sword. He shouted, "Don't harm yourself man! No one has escaped." There was just no way! But indeed, when I had my servants bring in the torches, sure enough, everyone was present and accounted for. To be honest, this scared me more than the earthquake. Think about it! I wasn't dealing here with the wrath of Rome, but the hand of the living God! I fell at their feet and asked how I could be saved.

I took them home with me. They told me about Jesus the Christ. Why should I as a Roman accept a crucified Jew as Lord? Paul and Silas put it in terms I could understand. Jesus' atonement mirrored my predicament earlier that evening. That is, we were all prisoners to sin, but Jesus took on himself all our punishment on a cross, so that we could escape and be free. Paradoxically, God spoke in an earthquake that day as well.

Paul asked if I believed. I did. He asked if I was ready to become a prisoner of Jesus. I was. Not only I, but my entire household with me, my wife, kids, servants and associates. We gave our lives to Christ and were immersed that very hour of the night in the very pool where we had washed the wounds of Paul and Silas. It was time to celebrate. We had a feast of love and joy. In that very meal Paul showed us how to remember the Lord Jesus.

I was now a Christian, but I was still the jailer. It broke my heart to put my teachers back behind bars. You can imagine my joy when the magistrates sent for them to be released the next morning. You can also imagine my consternation when they refused. "NO!" Paul said, "They beat us publically without a trial. They treated us like criminals even though we are Roman citizens. Now they want to get rid of us quietly? No way! Let the leaders come here, escort us out themselves and apologize publically!"

When the officers told the magistrates that Paul and Silas were citizens, they freaked out. Do you realize how much trouble they could have been in? They could lose their jobs, pensions, and be beaten themselves. Why, if push came to shove, the entire town could be stripped of its status as a Roman colony. Paul had them behind the eight ball and he knew it. I was just lovin' it!

You should have seen those guys grovel! It was a great moment! "Please accept our sincerest apologies," they begged. "Please feel free to leave the jail . . . in fact, it might be best for all involved if you would leave the county." Paul replied nonchalantly, "Oh, I don't know . . . I might like to stick around a bit longer. I at least need to visit my sisters and brothers in the church – you know who I'm talking about don't you? I do certainly hope you don't give them any problems after I'm gone." Paul was enjoying himself; the magistrates weren't so much. He wasn't being vindictive or playing mind games. He was protecting God's people. It was essential for the community to see that we were not an illegal sect. It was important that they saw Paul and Silas vindicated publically as Roman citizens. They had to know that they were not run out of town as renegades.

I'll tell you, it worked too. Our church began to grow like mad. Paul, Silas and Timothy went on to Thessalonica, Berea, Athens and Corinth. We sent them with our blessings and chased them with our financial support. Several times we took up a substantial love offering for them and sent it through Epaphroditus. Lydia was usually the instigator of these gifts.

They left Luke behind to get us on our feet. Under his leadership Clement and I and several other men were trained to be elders. There have been pressures from without and interpersonal conflicts from within. Yet, as Paul modeled for us, whether we are rich or poor, comfortable or in conflict, we can do all things through Jesus Christ who strengthens us. We put no confidence in our own flesh. Rather we humble ourselves as did Jesus, before whom every knee shall bow. So we rejoice in all circumstances and are anxious in none. For in prayer and thanksgiving we eagerly await the return of Jesus. In the mean-time, the peace of God which transcends all understanding, stands watch over the hearts and minds of his church here at Philippi.

June 19, A.D. 51

Dear Luke,

My name is Jason. I'm a friend of Paul, Silas and Timothy and a brother in the Lord Jesus Christ. Paul asked me to write you this letter and give you an update on their situation and location. After leaving you, they arrived here in Thessalonica, having passed through Amphipolis and Apollonia via the *Ignatian Way*. At first they were accepted with enthusiasm in the synagogue. For three weeks Paul lectured on the Scriptures, demonstrating with passage after passage that Jesus was the Christ and that it was necessary for him to suffer death and be raised again. His lectures were electrifying. Tension began to build, however, when Paul talked about Gentiles being included in the Kingdom of God. As the tensions grew, so did the crowds. Even pagans began to abandon their idols and listen to Paul lecture.

Well, when the Jews saw this mongrel crowd in their synagogue they got rather irate with Paul. But what could they do? They couldn't fire him. My goodness, we tried to pay him for his services, but he refused. He would work long days and then teach in the evenings. He was a great example to those among us who tend to be a bit lazy. He didn't get to all the sluggards, however. I suppose that's why they got to him.

Let me explain. The Jews got jealous of Paul's popularity and indignant when he treated pagans as if they were as good as Jews, as if they were welcome to God. So these rabble rousers went to the marketplace and rounded up a bunch of scallywags. These lazy sluggards are too tired or sick to work but always manage to muster the energy for a party or a fight. Normally the Jews wouldn't associate with these vermin. But since they wanted Paul punished, it seemed expedient to utilize their services.

It didn't take much to whip this crew up into a lather. They stormed through the streets shouting obscenities and curses against Paul. Twisted half-truths and innuendo can gather quite a crowd. By the time they surrounded my house they were at a fever pitch. Praise God, Paul wasn't there. They would have torn him limb from limb. It was just nuts! They grabbed me and several other brothers who were in the house and dragged us before the city officials. They accused Paul of turning the world upside down. What could I say? "Guilty as charged!" But in an upside down world, Paul was merely turning things right side up. They went on to accuse him of high treason, acclaiming a king other than Caesar. They just didn't understand that Christianity was about a spiritual kingdom. I tried to explain, but to no avail. It was all I could do to talk them out of a lynching. I had to pay a pretty fair bond to settle them down and to assure them that we would take care of the situation.

When Paul returned and learned what I had done he was fit to be tied. He didn't want me "wasting" my money like that. He felt almost as if I had betrayed him and hindered his work in Thessalonica. In fact, he said this whole thing was a plot from the Devil. I know Paul was upset, but looking back on it, I still think I did the right thing.

That night, as soon as it got dark, we whisked Paul away with many tears, not least of which were his. They went to Berea. It is a sleepy little town off the beaten path. Timothy has already returned to us and informed us that Paul made it there safely.

Luke, all these affairs have convinced us that we are in the last days. Lawless men have risen among us, even from our own countrymen, to oppose us. Like the Jews of Judea and the prophets of old, we suffer from our own people. Nonetheless, we expect to be caught up in the air with our soon coming king. It is the hope of his appearing that sustains us in these dark days. Even though we are oppressed, the church continues to grow and mature. For this reason, we pray continually awaiting the blessed hope of our coming savior, the Lord Jesus Christ.

Enduring for His Name,

Jason

July 30, A.D. 51

From: Timothy
To: Luke

We thank our God every time we remember you in our prayers. We ask that he fill you with the knowledge of his will and great patience and endurance in the work of his glorious kingdom. We rejoiced to hear through Epaphroditus how well the church is doing, even under adverse circumstances. Tell them that their generous gifts were a great blessing to the foundling church at Thessalonica. Your kindness and sacrifice allowed us to preach instead of make tents. This was especially helpful since our time in Thessalonica was cut short.

That's why I am writing to you, Luke, to let you know where you can contact us. Jason told you that we fled to Berea. We had been hunkered down there for several weeks when Paul's curiosity got the better of him. He just had to know how the Thessalonians were doing. So he wrote them a letter and told me to deliver it. That made sense. I had better legs than Silas and the mob wasn't after me. Off I went. After several weeks of encouraging the brothers and helping with leadership training, I returned to Berea. How could I know that I was being followed? I just feel sick to my stomach over it. (This is the kind of thing that could give a guy an ulcer! Paul tells me I need to learn to relax and drink a bit more wine. I would be interested in your professional opinion.) Perhaps I should have been more careful, but it never crossed my mind that they would go to such great lengths out of jealousy and hatred. It was an honest mistake from youthful inexperience. To make a long story short, some of these trouble-makers followed me back to Berea and broke up our meetings there.

That just broke our hearts because the Berean synagogue was about the only place we have ever been welcomed. Man, it was awesome. From the very first Sabbath they embraced us with open arms. They went crazy over Paul's teaching. As soon as he announced what passage he was going to discuss, the *Chazan* would roll the scroll to the right place so the leaders could read along. They soaked in the word of God like parched ground soaks in water. They weren't satisfied with weekly Bible studies. They would come by the Synagogue before work each morning. And we had home Bible studies every night of the week. Many of the Jews embraced their Messiah. Moreover, a great number of prominent Greek women in the city also flocked to the church. Already we are seeing many of their husbands, officials and dignitaries, accept Christ and join our meetings.

When those troublemakers showed up from Thessalonica, they accused Paul of all kinds of things. They said he stirred up riots (look who's talking!). They charged the Christians with heresy, blasphemy, lewd love-feasts, even cannibalistic sacraments. The whole of their charges were ludicrous and dismissed easily enough. But one thing we couldn't deny was the anger they engendered in the crowds. Paul's life was once again in danger.

It was the same old song and dance. Paul was run out of town. That night the brothers escorted him to the coast. Early the next morning they set sail for Athens before the lynch mob even knew he was gone. Perhaps 200 miles will keep them at bay.

Paul's whereabouts were kept in strict confidence. In fact, Silas and I weren't even sure where he was until his escort returned and told us that Paul wanted us to come to him as soon as possible. It's been several weeks now and I'm getting ready to pack my bags and go find him. I've asked the brothers at Thessalonica to contribute to the mission and now I'm asking you. If you want to get in on the giving you'll have to act fast. We won't be here much more than another week or two. We still have some teacher-training to finish and a leadership retreat. (Boy do I feel inadequate for all this. I'm too young to be teaching these Elders). Because of the Berean's interest in the Scriptures, we are progressing quickly. As soon as the leadership team is established we'll be gone. When we locate Paul we'll send you a full report. Meanwhile, may the grace of our Lord Jesus Christ be with you.

Timothy, "son" of Paul

THE TESTIMONY OF AN AREOPAGITE
By Dionysius of Athens

Athens, the prize of prattlers, is my home. Our population is smaller than our reputation. That is, for a town just over 10,000 we have done well in the field of Philosophy. In fact, we are the Mecca of the intellectual world, the most prized university in the Empire. It is a reputation well deserved. From Attica's cape came Socrates, Plato, Aristotle, Aristophanes, Epicurus, Zeno and a host of other renowned minds. I, Dionysius, am among the leading thinkers of my day, a member of the elite 30 man Areopagus council.

Naturally, we are used to ambitious young upstarts coursing through our hallowed halls seeking a hearing and gathering about themselves a class of ambling disciples. Just about any sort of vagabond can create a crowd in our city with the least bit of oratory skill. String together an idea or two and "Voila´," you have yourself an entourage of "wanna be's".

Few of these survive long, however. They just can't compete with the "big" boys. To make much headway, you have to belong to either the Stoics or the Epicureans. Both movements seek to liberate one from fate through an ethical system which frees us from potentially unpleasant circumstances. Yet they go about that in very different ways. The Epicureans believe that the greatest good is in pleasure. They do recognize, however, that crass indulgence is to be avoided because it usually leads to pain. For instance, they wouldn't sleep with another man's wife if there were a strong possibility of getting caught and beaten. Nor would they promote debauchery if it came with a hangover. Yet, at the risk of oversimplification, their motto is: "If it feels good do it." They are practical atheists and rational hedonists.

We Stoics, on the other hand, approach life from a different tack. We suggest that the greatest good comes from detachment. To paraphrase Seneca: If you succumb to pain or sorrow, you will be robbed of the greatest good. If you love things too much, and they are lost or broken, you will be overwhelmed with grief. At the risk of oversimplification, we suggest that no pain *is* gain, and no pleasure means no disappointment. Therefore, don't laugh, cry, grimace or giggle and you will find the greatest good in life. Paul, who grew up in Tarsus, fertile soil for our philosophy, is obviously familiar with our views. He even quoted one of our poets in his speech here.

In walks Paul, a Hellenistic Jew. Please understand, Greeks are no more prejudiced against Jews than any other "inferior" race (a view not dissimilar to Palestinian Jews'). We think Hebrews are a bit barbaric for practicing circumcision. They are thought to be uncultured and antisocial for abandoning the theater, the Olympics, and the finer things afforded by Greek language and life. Even so, Paul got as fair a hearing as any other babbler would in the marketplace of ideas. In fact, he may have had an advantage since we are somewhat familiar with Moses, Solomon, Philo and other great Jewish minds.

Paul's zeal immediately attracted attention. He was all hot and bothered by the idols that lined our streets. Indeed Petronius spoke truth when he said that it is easier to find a god in Athens than a man. Yet we thought Paul was making much ado about nothing. Even we didn't take our gods too seriously. Like Philo, and to some extent Paul himself, we were allegorists with our sacred texts. Our modern intellect had allowed us to outgrow much of our superstitious theism.

What got our attention most was the large number of students Paul attracted to his soap-box. Some of our leaders went over to check him out. Our response was classic Greek curiosity bathed in skepticism and peppered with cynicism. He was talking about resurrection. We couldn't tell if he meant a literal bodily resurrection (perish the thought!), or some kind of philosophic category. But it was apparent that we needed a more formal hearing of his views. So we invited him to defend himself before the Areopagus.

We opened the hearing by inviting Paul to elucidate his ideas about "resurrection." These were strange thoughts indeed. We didn't much believe what Paul was saying, but if Athenians are anything, they are curious, especially when it comes to philosophic novelty. Demosthenes spoke truly of us: "You are the best people at being deceived by something new that is said."

Paul's opening was really quite clever. He said, "I see that you are a very religious people." Depending on the context he could either be insulting us as superstitious or complimenting us as devout. From the start we listened intently in order to discern his meaning. Then he played off an idol we erected to an unknown god. It was kind of a catch-all idol in case some obscure god got offended at our neglect to recognize him/her.

"Let me tell you about this God of which you seem to be ignorant," Paul said. Right then I thought, "This guy is smooth." As Greeks, we consider it almost a sin to be ignorant of anything. This became the springboard for his discourse on Yahweh, the creator God of the Hebrews. As Stoics, we agreed with Paul about creation *ex nihilo* rather than the evolution of the cosmos. He presented God as creator, sustainer, ruler, father and judge. We might have dismissed Paul as just another parochial Jew, but he was obviously well read. He quoted not one but two of our poets in his address. From Epimenides he borrowed the line: "In him we live and move and have our being." And from the Cilician poet Aratus in his *Phaenomena* (also cited in *Hymn of Zeus*), Paul used the phrase: "We are his offspring." Both of these he applied to Yahweh. Since Paul agreed with us, against the Epicureans, we decided that he made much sense. If we are offspring of God, then why should we demean him with images of gold and silver, wood and stone. Certainly God is not less than we ourselves. It struck me, perhaps for the first time, that God is a reality to whom we will all be accountable.

Paul's timing was impeccable. He moved right from the nature of God to the coming judgment. Then, just when I was thinking, "OK, give me some hard, cold evidence to believe," Paul talked about the raising of Jesus of Nazareth from the dead. Few took him seriously. Most sneered vocally. But I thought, "Wait a minute! If this is true then it changes everything." I pressed him on the subject. "Just to be sure we're on the same page," said I, "we're not talking about a philosophic category here; we're talking about a literal bodily resurrection." "Yes," Paul replied, "I saw it with my own eyes and others touched him, watched him consume a piece of fish, listened to him speak. Why, there were over five hundred who saw him on a single occasion, most of whom are still alive and can testify to what they saw, should you care to accompany me to Palestine."

Paul was finished at the Areopagus. In fact, he was kind of dismissed. But I wasn't finished with him yet. I am well over sixty years old and in all my days I had never heard such ideas. I followed Paul with a few others, including my escort, a woman named Damaris. We not only listened to Paul, we became obedient to the gospel and the church of Athens was born. We are a small fringe movement here in this intellectual center, yet we stand firm in the truth. I'll tell you this: We are few, not because Christianity is intellectually untenable, but because the intellectual elite are arrogant, bigoted and impermeable. I say this as an insider. To most of the Areopagites and their ilk, religion is not about truth. It is a game that is played for the entertainment of its participants. A good chess match would accomplish the same purpose. Little do they know just how high the stakes are and how low they'll be brought if they refuse to repent. Jesus said of a truth, "The way is narrow and few are those who find it."

I get the feeling that Paul was a bit disappointed in the outcome of his sermon. I for one, however, was delighted. Oh sure, I too wish more had responded positively to the gospel. At the same time I would hate to think that Paul considered me a waste of time. I will be eternally grateful that I was shown the light of life. I may only be one, but I am one whom God loves. I am one to whom the unknown God has become very personal indeed.

January 25, A.D. 52

To: Luke
From: Sosthenes

Greetings in the precious name of our Lord Jesus Christ. Our brother Paul asked that I write to you and let you know he is headed for Ephesus and from there he hopes to make it to Jerusalem by the feast of Passover. He has had a fruitful ministry even in a city as shamefully corrupt as ours.

Paul arrived here from Athens. I got acquainted with him early since I was one of the primary leaders of the synagogue. It was not uncommon for us to have visitors in our city since we are the main sea port of Achaia. We pride ourselves in being the commercial capital of the Empire. Furthermore, since Claudius' edict to ban Jewish worship in Rome, we have a considerable number of new faces in our synagogue. I'm sure you've heard of Priscilla and Aquila, Paul's new business partners. Together they are making tents and building churches.

Paul, however, stood out since he was a Rabbi trained under Gamaliel. We were glad to have him preach for us. To be honest, however, he was somewhat of a disappointment. We've heard men who were more eloquent. Besides, he seemed to have a one track mind. All he wanted to do was talk about Messiah, and how Jesus of Nazareth, crucified by the Romans, fulfilled that role. Week after week it was the same thing. Pretty soon along came a couple of Paul's students, Silas and Timothy. They brought a pretty fair sum of money with them from Berea, Thessalonica, and I believe your congregation there in Philippi. Suddenly, Paul didn't need to make tents for a living and began singing his single verse of Jesus, Jesus, Jesus every day, all day long.

You know how irritating that can be! What's worse is that he started inviting a bunch of Gentiles (no offense, brother). Now, I'm not a bigot, mind you, but our little synagogue just wasn't ready for that. We told him gently to back off, but that just seemed to push him farther and faster ahead. It finally came down to a face to face public confrontation. Do you know what that rascal did? He took off his cloak and shook it at us. For a Jew that is a pretty serious insult. He said, "Your blood be on your own heads! I am clear of my responsibility." From then on he taught Gentiles almost exclusively.

It wouldn't have been so bad if he hadn't taken up teaching right next door to the synagogue in the home of "Gaius" Titius Justus a former proselyte in our synagogue. Talk about tensions! To make matters worse, he also baptized Crispus who just happened to be the synagogue ruler and my own mentor. It was then that I took over the leadership of the synagogue. Our services dwindled after Crispus, Gaius and their families converted. Many of my flock flocked to Paul. I didn't know what to do. I was torn between my love for the synagogue and my love for Crispus, between my love for truth that I saw in Paul and my love for tradition and cultural purity that I saw in the hardliners still left in the synagogue.

They were growing, we were waning. I tried to hide my wavering behind a confident and often vehement exterior. The more they grew the angrier we got and the more deliberate our slander became. A number of us would have gladly taken Paul out, given him the beating of his life, and sent him away from our city. Little did we know that he was under the protection of the Lord Jesus. In fact, Christ appeared to Paul in a vision one night and told him that he would not be attacked in Corinth as he had been so many other places. This only fanned Paul into a full flaming fury. After a year and a half we just had to do something!

Instead of taking matters into our own hands, we decided to take him to court. Gallio, the younger brother of Seneca, was proconsul at the time. Although he didn't much favor the Jews, we felt that he was fair enough to hear our case. We presented to him a well-reasoned charge against Paul who was advocating a new and illicit religion. We knew Paul was going to counter with the argument that Christianity was merely the logical extension of Judaism. We would then cross-counter by showing all the marked differences between Judaism and the Way: Sunday worship, abandonment of circumcision and the law, rebellious belief in a Messiah deemed by Rome as a political threat, etc.

Unfortunately (depending on which side you're on), our case never got that far. In fact, Paul opened his mouth to make his defense when Gallio spoke up, "If you Jews were making a complaint about some misdemeanor or serious crime, it would be reasonable for me to listen to you. But since it involves questions about words and names and your own law — settle the matter yourselves. I will not be a judge of such things." With that Gallio dismissed us with the wave of his hand.

I couldn't leave, however. There was too much at stake. If I just walked away, my comrades would know I was secretly waffling between the synagogue and the church. I pressed my case with Gallio and pressed my luck a bit too far. The Greeks, who are usually antagonistic against God's people, took advantage of this volatile situation and attacked me right there in front of the judge's bench. Gallio didn't even care. He let them have their moment of boyish pleasure and then simply said, "Get this bloody spectacle out of my sight." That was shocking enough. What was worse was the response of my kinsmen. They bludgeoned me with their words more brutally than the Greeks had with their fists. They accused me of secretly subverting the case, of presenting it badly on purpose so as to allow Paul to escape unpunished. This is not what I needed! Over the next several days, I mulled it over in my mind. It occurred to me that Paul was right, not only doctrinally, but in the way he treated people. I took a gamble when I knocked on Titius Justus' door. To my delight, they opened it wide and welcomed me into their fellowship.

I'll be the first to admit that the church has its problems. Here in Corinth you are bound to have maturity problems and moral problems, even among the people of God. Add to that the tensions of our Jew/Gentile mix, our rich/poor mix, etc. and you can guess the kinds of difficulties we face. We may have a long way to go, but at least we are on the right track. This church offers the correct faith. It offers true hope. But above these, it offers unconditional love. That is the greatest of all.

My Witnesses

August 30, A.D. 53

To: Paul
From: Priscilla

Greetings in the precious name of our Lord and Savior Jesus Christ. We pray that God grants you safety during your stay in Jerusalem. We know what a dangerous place that is for you.

Has your hair grown back yet from your haircut in Cenchrea? I know it was necessary for your vow, but as quickly as you're going bald you may never see that hair again.

I'm writing to tell you how much everyone still misses you in Ephesus. They are eager for you to come back. Just as you were well received in the synagogue at Berea, you are still warmly received here. As you said, "If it is the Lord's will, I will return." Well, we believe it is the Lord's will. After all, there are many Jews in this place who are eager to study the Word and are open to the idea of Gentile evangelism. Aquila and I continue to lay a foundation for you so that when you come your harvest will be plentiful.

We did have one interesting encounter we thought you should be prepared for. A young man named Apollos came through town. He is a wonderful young preacher from Alexandria and very charismatic. He is well educated and has a zeal for the word. He preaches Jesus with accuracy and passion. The only problem was that he had never learned about Christian baptism. He was still promoting the baptism of John the Baptist.

We had him over to the house and taught him the difference between the two. At first he was puzzled. He couldn't understand what the difference was or why it was important. After all, both are immersions in water for the forgiveness of sins. We pointed out, however, that Jesus' baptism was not a ceremonial washing but obedience prompted by faith. That is, baptism is an enacted prayer of a penitent sinner, an acceptance of and imitation of the death, burial and resurrection of Jesus. Then his eyes began to brighten. When we showed how Jesus' baptism involved the Holy Spirit whereas John's did not, a lightbulb came on. He grasped the concept that John's baptism was a good deed done for the love of God, but Christian baptism was God's good work in us done out of love for his children. We had to clarify for him that baptism adds nothing to the cross of Christ except our willingness to accept it.

Apollos is a sharp young preacher. Frankly, I was surprised that a man of his intellect and skill would so humbly accept such correction, especially since it came from a woman, but he did. He was more concerned with pleasing God than winning an argument. For him, truth is more valuable than pride. It was a delightful meeting for all three of us.

Anyway, since Aquila and I have things pretty much under control here, we told him about the needs in Corinth. Paul, things are getting a bit messy over there. Apollos was eager to go and try to provide some stability to their situation. So we sent him with our blessing and with a letter of introduction so the people of Corinth would receive him. Even now he is over there trying to iron out a few sticky problems. I don't mean to alarm you, Paul, but your work here is not finished. We need you to return as soon as possible.

In submission to God,

Priscilla

My Witnesses

February 14, A.D. 54

Dear Tyrannus,

As a fellow teacher and Christian brother, I need to ask you to help me with a pressing issue. It appears that Paul's followers are in competition with mine both here in Corinth and in Ephesus. I suspect that the real issue is parochial pride, which has no place in the church. Nevertheless, the theological smoke screen used for dissension is this issue of baptism. I will do what I can to squelch the squabbles here in Achaia if you will do your part there in Asia. Please read the following letter to your classes at your earliest convenience.

To my former students: I am genuinely flattered that you consider yourselves to be my disciples. But get over it and grow up. We are disciples of Jesus Christ alone. As the Lord himself said, none should be called "Father," or "Teacher," or "Master." Paul and I are both servants of Christ. It matters not who baptized you or trained you in the faith. Stop with the cliques, the gossip, and the factions. Though I've not yet met Paul I consider him a beloved brother and a colleague of high esteem. In fact, he is an Apostle of Jesus Christ; I am not. He therefore deserves your respect and attention. If you have an opportunity to avail yourselves of his teaching and choose not to, I consider you a fool.

It has come to my attention that Paul baptized twelve of my former students into Christ. Why does this bother you? I only led them to John the Baptist. They needed to commit their lives to Christ by becoming obedient in Christian baptism. Didn't John himself say, "He must increase and I must decrease"? Are you ashamed that they went on to submit to Christ? Don't you understand? This is what I, myself, would have told them to do. This is the example I set for you after Priscilla and Aquila shared with me this precious gift of God. It is truth that we must seek, not party lines.

Are you offended that they received the Holy Spirit after being immersed? Or perhaps you are offended that they were granted the gift of tongues and prophecy through the laying on of the Apostle's hands? Let me set the record straight. There is no other practice in the Christian Church but to immerse penitent believers into Christ. Now let's stop following divisive parties and simply do what the Apostles taught, what Jesus himself modeled. Baptism is a visible proclamation to God of our willingness to die to self and a plea to be raised with Christ to walk in a new life. You should be ashamed of yourselves for rejecting this precious gift of God so that you can distinguish yourselves as a unique sect!

I understand that Paul is beginning to experience some opposition from the Jews in the synagogue. After three months of persuasive preaching I'm not surprised that they are beginning to malign the Way. One can only ignore Christianity for so long. Don't you dare align yourselves with the synagogue rather than the church. We belong to Christ and his one body. Fight for unity, not against it.

If you believe me to teach the truth, if you esteem me as a man of God, then heed my advice and throw your support behind Paul, submit to his teaching, and above all, retain the unity of the one true church.

Sincerely,

Apollos

My Witnesses

Seven Streakers Lead to Book Burning
By Kalos Thomas

There have been multiple unsubstantiated reports of extraordinary miracles being done here in Ephesus. Apparently Paul of Tarsus, a prominent Jewish rabbi from Jerusalem, has been touring Asia, Macedonia and Achaia, creating quite a stir with his uncanny abilities. Inside sources say he healed a lame man at Lystra, cast out a demon at Philippi, and struck a man blind on Cyprus. He is a controversial figure who has been brought before the city officials at Philippi, Corinth, and Athens. Furthermore he was chased out of Damascus, Jerusalem, Pisidian Antioch, Iconium, Lystra, Thessalonica and Berea.

His track record in Ephesus has been no different. Since he arrived last spring he has generated both strong support and opposition. The Jewish synagogue no longer allows him to lecture there. He has therefore taken up teaching in the school of Tyrannus. As Paul's opposition rises, so does his apparent ability to perform miracles. Recently some claimed to have been healed by the mere touch of Paul's tent-shop aprons. It was his laundry lady who first noticed the power in Paul's garments. She claims that after washing his apron one day, she felt a tingling sensation in her arthritic hands. She has been painfully crippled for years. You can call it coincidence or you can believe in a miracle, but her physician has verified that she is completely healed.

As rumors of Paul's abilities began to circulate, more and more people flocked to see him. When they did, he always spoke to them about one Jesus of Nazareth whom Paul believes is the Jewish Messiah and the Son of God come to earth. "It was he," Paul said, "who healed you, not I. He is the great physician who will heal your souls as well as your bodies. Repent of your sins and put your faith in Jesus Christ." Well, large numbers have gone after him. Others are still just curious onlookers.

Among those who were mere spectators are the seven sons of Sceva, the high priest. They have been known to exorcize demons. Much of their power apparently comes from invoking the names of powerful magicians or religious figures of the past who can overpower the demon on behalf of the victim. These seven young men encountered a particularly powerful demon just three days ago. Their normal incantations were ineffective. Therefore, they used the name of Jesus whom Paul preaches. Eyewitnesses report that the demon spoke directly to them. He said, "Jesus I know, and I know about Paul, but who are *you?*"

At that the demoniac attacked the seven men. He single-handedly stripped them naked and beat them bloody. They fled from the house and through the streets of Ephesus. Needless to say, seven bloody streakers attracted a bit of attention. It didn't take long for this rumor to spread. The name of Jesus was soon revered for its extraordinary power.

Those who had become followers of Christ brought out their magic scrolls and burned them. This has created an uproar in the cultic community since many of these scrolls contained secret incantations and magical formulae that will be lost forever. These works were highly prized. In fact one expert we talked to estimated the total value of their books at well over $3,000,000. These Christians are being called right-wing fundamentalist anti-cultural book burners.

One reporter who was at the bonfire asked why these books weren't sold and the money given to the poor. The leading Christians vehemently replied, "God hates sorcery. We must not spread this evil. These black arts destroy lives and must therefore themselves be destroyed. Ill gotten gain is a shameful foundation for benevolence. If you don't like this book burning, you should see the fire God has in store for those who use these books!"

Some accuse Paul of brainwashing these Christians and even practicing sorcery himself. Whether his power is "from above" is still being debated, but this much seems clear – Paul has now made adversaries both in the Jewish community and in the parascientific community. This is not likely the last report we'll hear about this man here in Ephesus.

My Witnesses

A Report by Protagoras, City Clerk of Ephesus
November 30, A.D. 55

This notice will serve as a citation against Demetrius the silversmith and a potential report to the proconsul should such action become necessary. The following statement will explain the events that took place this afternoon in our city, and how I, Protagoras, dismissed the unruly crowd, averting a potential disturbance.

Some two years ago an itinerant Jewish philosopher by the name of Paul of Tarsus arrived in our city. He had gathered about himself both Jews and Greeks, astounding some with his magical powers and enamoring others with his oratory skill. He even attracted the attention of such dignitaries as Erastus, the "Director of Public Works" in Corinth.

Paul was thrown out of his own Jewish synagogue because of his fraternizing with the Greeks. He also made enemies among the Greeks because he taught them to abandon the temples. Nevertheless, none of his actions were illegal, nor did he endanger the peace of our city. He is indeed a public pest, but he's done nothing of a criminal nature.

Because so many of our citizens have followed Paul, the temple artisans began to experience a severe decline in their profits. Demetrius, one of the leading silversmiths of the goddess Artemis, became irate over his drop in income. He rallied the silversmiths in the union and slandered Paul as an atheistic heretic who taught people here in Ephesus, as well as all parts of Asia, that man-made gods are no gods at all. Demetrius whipped them up into a lather, convincing them that the worship of Her Divine Majesty is in jeopardy. That was enough to get them chanting: "Great is Artemis of the Ephesians!"

They took their fervor to the streets. Soon they had gathered a parade of people who apparently thought this was part and parcel of the Artemisian festival which is currently going on in our city. Soon the whole town was in an uproar. First they went to where Paul was staying. He wasn't home. So they seized two of his companions, Gaius of Derbe and Aristarchus of Thessalonica. It was about that time that I caught wind of these events and went to investigate. By the time I caught up with the mob, they were already in the theater. Paul, I later found out, actually wanted to enter the theater and address the crowd. That would have been certain suicide. Thankfully he was hindered by his own disciples and several dignitaries who are visiting Ephesus for the festival. These magistrates happen to be friends of Paul and were able to detain him. It is a good thing too, otherwise this report *would* have to be sent to the governor because of an illegal lynching.

Once I arrived at the theater, I began asking people what was going on. No one seemed to know. They were just along for the ride. All they knew was that they were upset and it had something to do with defending the great goddess Diana. Some shouted one thing, others another. Pretty soon someone pushed Alexander to the front. He was a Jewish leader in the synagogue. Apparently many people still did not differentiate between the Christian movement and the Jewish synagogue. Alexander was trying to explain that the Jews were not responsible – that they were not and should not be connected with Paul and the Christians. Granted, many people assumed they were. After all, everyone knew how both Jews and Christians avoided our temples and abstained from Greek worship.

When Alexander motioned for them to be silent the crowd went wild. In unison they shouted, "Great is Artemis of the Ephesians." This lasted for the better part of two hours! I kept expecting someone to bring clarity to the situation. Finally I just had to put a stop to it before somebody got hurt and things got really out of hand. I rose and quieted the crowd. They knew they better listen to me because I have the authority to write a report to Rome about such situations incriminating those rabble-rousers who were responsible. When I had their attention I said, "Men of Ephesus, doesn't all the world know that the city of Ephesus is the guardian of the temple of the great Artemis and of her image, which fell from heaven? Therefore, since these facts are undeniable, you ought to be quiet and not do anything rash." Artemis is bigger than these itinerant preachers. It's not like they are going to eradicate her worship by promoting Jesus! I went on to say, "You have brought these men here, though they have neither robbed temples nor blasphemed our goddess." They were a nuisance to our city, but they were not criminals. So I warned Demetrius not to take the law into his own hands but to take these men to court if indeed he had any substantial legal charge against them. After all, Helius and Celer sit as proconsuls over our jurisdiction. Moreover, we have legal assemblies three times a month to consider such affairs. This was not the time nor the place. Finally, I told them, "As it is, we are in danger of being charged with rioting because of today's events. In that case we would not be able to account for this commotion, since there is no reason for it." After I said this I glared at Demetrius, insinuating that his name would be placed at the top of the report which I would send to Rome. His eyes indicated that he understood. He rose and walked out of the theater, his fellow workers in his wake. With that the crowd disbanded peaceably.

I expect no further incident regarding this fellow Paul of Tarsus. It is my understanding that he is packing his bags, getting ready to leave our city. The reports I have indicate that he has already sent a couple of his envoys ahead of him into Macedonia where he will spend a short time before returning to Jerusalem for Passover. Rumor has it that he would eventually like to take his show to Rome. If he makes it, I suspect he will have a more "vivid" reception there than he has had even here in Ephesus.

A Travel Log from Aristarchus

The following is an account of our trip from Ephesus to Jerusalem in the Winter of 56 and Spring of 57.

Participants:

	Berea:	Sopater son of Pyrrhus
	Thessalonica:	Aristarchus & Secundus
	Philippi:	Luke
	Derbe:	Gaius
	Lystra:	Timothy
	Asia:	Tychicus and Trophimus

Itinerary:

Phase 1: From Ephesus to Macedonia, encouraging the brothers.

Phase 2: From Macedonia to Achaia, wintered in Greece for three months. As we were about to set sail for Syria a plot against Paul was discovered. So we abandoned the ship (with the assassins still on it) and set out by foot back through Macedonia. I'm sure the assassins were more than mildly disappointed when they discovered our absence.

Phase 3: We went on ahead to Troas while Paul went to Philippi to pick up Luke. They celebrated Passover together. Five days later they met us at Troas where we stayed seven days. Aside from the Eutychus incident, it was a pleasant visit with the church there and a nice reunion with Luke's old friends and family.

Phase 4: We set sail for Assos where we were to pick up Paul. He insisted on walking from Troas, some twenty miles. He said something about unwinding after his all night sermon. From there we passed to Mitylene and the next day arrived at Kios. The day after that we crossed over to Samos and the following day arrived at Miletus. It was here that Paul sent for the Elders of Ephesus to meet us. It was thirty five miles from Miletus to Ephesus, so it took us four days to retrieve the Elders from there. Paul was right. Had we gone to Ephesus we would have spent much more time than that. Ephesus was where Paul had his longest ministry and there simply would have been too many people to see and too much hospitality to refuse. It was better this way. Even so, when we knelt on the beach together for one final prayer, we had to tear ourselves apart with many tears.

Phase 5: From Troas we sailed straight to Cos. The following day we went to Rhodes and from there to Patara. There we boarded a ship that was crossing over to Phoenicia. After sighting Cyprus and passing to the south of it, we sailed on to Syria. We landed at Tyre where our ship unloaded its cargo. We stayed there a week, visiting the brothers. Some of these were old friends of Paul's and new ones of ours. It was a delightful stay and enlightening to meet foreign brothers who worship differently but love God equally. It reminds us that the Kingdom is bigger than our local congregations. When the Holy Spirit revealed to them that Paul's life would be in danger in Jerusalem they urged him not to go. He wouldn't hear of it. He simply lifted up his cloak and displayed his scars like badges. He asked, "Does this look like I'm afraid of a little pain?" He continued, "How will the gospel be spread if we don't share in Christ's suffering? This is my honor. I bear in my body the brand marks of Jesus." On we went. At the beach there were many more tears as we again knelt and prayed.

Phase 6: From Tyre we landed at Ptolemais where we met more brothers. We could only stay a day. In the morning we raced to Caesarea. We met Philip, a veteran Evangelist and one of the earliest disciples. He had four virgin daughters, each of whom had the gift of prophecy. We were there several days. Again they tried to persuade Paul not to go to Jerusalem. This time a prophet named Agabus came up from Jerusalem to help us. He was an old friend of Paul's. Agabus took Paul's belt and tied up his own hands and feet. The guy was really into this visual aid thing. He actually looked kind of silly. It reminded me of one of the O.T.

prophets who acted out what God told them to say. When Agabus got himself in a pretty good knot he looked at Paul and said, "In this way the Jews of Jerusalem will bind the owner of this belt and will hand him over to the Gentiles." At that we pleaded with Paul not to go. Luke reminded Paul that he did not have a promise from Jesus here in Jerusalem like he did in Corinth not to be beaten or killed. That seemed to get to him. Timothy said, "Paul, I'm not prepared to see you stoned as I did when I was a teenager. Please don't go." Paul, with tears in his eyes said, "Timothy, these are the scars that won your salvation. Do you think I would trade them for your soul?! I have labored now for two decades for people who are not my own. Will you now hinder me from suffering for my own people?! Why are you weeping and breaking my heart? I am ready not only to be bound but also to die in Jerusalem for the name of the Lord Jesus." We tried to argue with him that Agabus had a revelation from God that he shouldn't go. "NO!" Paul replied, "The revelation is that I would suffer, not that I shouldn't go." He was bound to become a martyr. So we gave up and said, "The Lord's will be done."

Phase 7: We packed our bags. The brothers who had just come from Jerusalem to see Paul escorted us to Mnason's house. He was a man from Cyprus and an early disciple. The following day we arrived in Jerusalem, in the nick of time for the feast of Pentecost.

My Witnesses

A Testimony from Eutychus

Have you ever had one of those dreams where you're falling but you wake up before you land? . . . I landed! My name is Eutychus and I hail from the small town of Troas, the gateway to Greece. It was the early Spring of 57 when Paul had come back to visit us. He brought with him Luke, our beloved physician. He had just finished a six year church planting campaign across the Aegean Sea in a Roman colony called Philippi. It was a wonderful reunion filled with tales and tears. At the end of seven days, our visit culminated in a worship service centering around the Lord's Supper at a "love feast."

It was Sunday evening. We all gathered in a third story apartment after everyone got off work. The place was packed. The whole church wanted to say "good-bye" to Paul and Luke before they got away the next morning. Paul, seeing the crowd, took the opportunity to preach. Boy did he preach! He went on until midnight. Now, I'm not trying to make excuses for myself, but that was way past my normal bed time. I fought off Mr. Sandman as long as I could, but the room was so stuffy. Aside from all those people packed in like sardines, there were a bunch of oil lamps to give us light. They also generated quite a bit of heat and smoke. They hazier the room got the drowsier I got. Finally I wallowed my way over to the window where I could get some fresh air. There was no place to sit or even stand. So I perched myself in the window sill. That was much better . . . for a while. But it didn't take long before I drifted into a deep sleep.

I guess that my body relaxed and I just slumped out the window. I remember dreaming that I was falling, falling, falling. Suddenly, but only for a split instance, I remember feeling a sharp pain in the back of my neck. Then I went completely blank. I could hear voices coming closer to me, like they were descending on me from above. I also remember that they sounded panicked and I wondered who was in trouble. I would like to give you more details but the whole thing is really pretty fuzzy.

They tell me that everyone rushed from the room and surrounded me. Luke worked his way through the crowd and checked me over. When he turned to my parents, long-time family friends, all he could say was, "I'm so sorry." It was then that Paul came to my side. He looked at Luke, then at my parents. They said it was almost as if they knew what Paul was thinking without him saying a word. He stretched his body out on top of mine – face to face and chest to chest. I remember feeling his breath on my face and . . . I can't explain it really. It was like I had been observing the scene from the perimeter of the crowd, like I wasn't really a part of it. Suddenly it was as if I was drawn from the perimeter to the ground, like I slipped under Paul's body at that moment. It was then that I began to feel the throbbing in my back and neck. I heard Paul say, "Don't be alarmed. He's alive!"

The crowd gasped, some because they believed Paul, and some because they didn't. When I stood and took a deep breath (you know, the kind you take when the wind is knocked out of you), the church broke out into spontaneous applause and cheers of joy. We went upstairs and celebrated the memorial meal of Jesus. I'll tell you, it was one great party!

Paul said later, "I don't know what came over me. I guess the Spirit just guided my mind and my steps. I wasn't purposely or presumptuously trying to imitate the great prophet, Elijah. It simply seemed right at the time." That night I think everyone was just glad to see me alive. It took a couple of days before it really sunk in that I had been raised from the dead. We had experienced a miracle of Biblical proportions! So what became of it? I was pretty stiff for several days. And I've never gotten over my fear of heights . . . but the church has. We have risen to new levels of faith and attendance. And as far as I know, I was the last person in Troas to fall asleep during a sermon.

A Critique of Paul's Sermon by Tychicus

Sermon Title: Church Leadership 101
Audience: Ephesian Elders while at Troas
Sermon Text: None

Sermon Outline:
1. A Review of Paul's Ministry in Ephesus
    a. Paul served the Ephesians with humility and tears, even through trials.
    b. Paul preached the full gospel of repentance and faith in Jesus both
        i. Publically and
        ii. Privately in homes
    c. Paul now will go to Jerusalem at the risk of physical danger and imprisonment
        i. He is compelled by the Spirit (or in his own spirit)
        ii. He is compelled to finish the task of preaching the gospel of God's grace
        iii. The Ephesians won't see Paul again.
        iv. Paul is innocent of their blood because he warned them of the wrath of God (an obvious allusion to Eze 3:17-19)
2. An Appeal to the Ephesian Elders to Do Their Work Well
    a. Keep watch over yourselves and over the flock
        i. Feed the Sheep of Jesus
        ii. Watch out for savage wolves (i.e. false teachers)
    b. Preach the Gospel in my stead
    c. Don't covet anyone's money
        i. I didn't while I was with you; rather I worked to provide a living for myself as well as my coworkers in the gospel.
        ii. For Jesus said, "It is more blessed to give than to receive."

A Review of Paul's Sermon:

A. Strengths:
1. Paul was very personable, almost to a fault. While he does seem to have a wonderful rapport with his audience, if he isn't careful he might be misconstrued as being egocentric since his message both begins and ends with personal illustrations which border on bragging.
2. His subject was perfectly matched for his audience and the situation at hand. He made good use of a teachable moment.
3. This message isn't merely appropriate to the Ephesian Elders, it is a model sermon for most Christian audiences. This message would serve well as a paradigm for preaching to believers.
4. Nice use of Biblical imagery, particularly the shepherd, sheep, wolf motif.
5. It was extremely practical. He gave his audience several things to put into practice when they went home.

B. Weaknesses:
1. Paul's exegesis wasn't just weak, it was non-existent. He made one allusion to Ezekiel 3:17-19, but there was no other Scripture used. Even his closing quote from the lips of Jesus isn't canonical (yet).
2. A three-point alliterative outline would help embed Paul's main points into his listeners' memory.
3. Paul's emotionalism may get the better of him. Tears are a great way of grabbing people's attention and getting them to focus on your message. But only up to a certain point. Too many tears become distracting. Furthermore, such emotive displays can leave the preacher open to criticism, especially of

trying to manipulate people's emotions rather than feeding them with substantive cognitive ideas.

4. Several of Paul's statements are unverifiable. For instance, he said that he would never see the Ephesians again. How can he know that? Or again, he said he was compelled by the Spirit to go to Jerusalem. How does he know it was the Holy Spirit and not his own spirit? Did he have a vision or a dream? Nothing in his message clarifies this point. Later still, Paul said that false teachers would afflict the church in Ephesus. Based on what empirical or sociological data can he make such a claim? Paul needs to be more careful to substantiate the claims he makes.

5. Point II B needs a bit more elaboration and clarification.

Overall Grade: B-

June 15, A.D. 57

An Open Letter from James, the Elder
To the Churches of Judea Which Are in Christ

I am writing to you to put to rest the rumors and half-truths that have been slung around the church concerning our dear brother Paul. Many of you have been told, or perhaps (God forbid), you have even spread the lie that Paul teaches the Jews who live among the Gentiles to abandon Moses' law and forbids them to circumcise their children. This is ludicrous and false. In fact, it was Paul who circumcised Timothy of Lystra because he was half-Jewish. He wanted Timothy to provide no offense to the synagogues of Asia as they preached the Gospel. Does this sound like the heretic you've heard about?

What Paul is doing is faithfully delivering the decree of the Jerusalem council stating that Gentiles do *not* have to become Jews in order to be Christians. This is a critical message because it deals with how we are saved. We do not add Jesus to Moses. Rather Moses' law leads us to Jesus and then we too must let it go (as a means of salvation). Indeed, our Gentile brothers must abstain from meat sacrificed to idols, blood, strangled animals and fornication, not as a means of earning God's favor but in order to maintain unity with their Jewish brothers.

Moreover, Paul, accompanied by eight men from Asia, Macedonia, and Achaia, brought gifts from their churches. This substantial gift will go a long way toward alleviating the suffering of our people. It took Paul over a year to prepare for, collect and deliver this offering. Does this sound like a man who has abandoned his Jewish brothers? Who among us can claim to match his efforts to love the Jews in such a tangible way?! Those who slander this brother are ignorant and hypocritical, and I challenge them to demonstrate greater orthodoxy than Paul.

Furthermore, when Paul arrived in Jerusalem, he came completing a vow he had taken in Cenchrea. He went to the temple and payed for his own purification rites as well as those of four other brothers who were also completing a vow. Paul is not speaking against the law of our people. On the contrary, he is upholding and practicing Mosaic ritual! Those who tell you otherwise are misinformed or malicious (or both).

The rumors about Paul have been exacerbated by his recent arrest. Let me set the record straight. Yes, Paul was accosted in the temple. Yes, he was nearly killed by an angry mob of Jewish worshipers. Yes, they accused him of escorting Trophimus, a Greek Christian from Asia, into the temple. However, that was *not* true. Indeed, Paul is close friends with Trophimus and they had spent much time together, even in our city. Paul treated him with the dignity a Christian brother deserves. They were *not*, however, in the temple together. How can I prove this? Very simply. If Trophimus was in the temple with Paul, why did they grab Paul and not Trophimus? It would have been the Gentile, not the Jew who broke the law and deserved the beating. "So why," I hear you ask, "was Paul arrested? What was his crime?" That is precisely what Claudius Lysias, the commander of Jerusalem's Roman troops, wanted to know. After several encounters, the Jews have still not given him a satisfactory answer.

Trophimus, however, has explained it clearly. He knows these Jews from Asia who started the riot against Paul. They are, he says, the leaders of the synagogue of Ephesus. They are still bitter about the conversion of so many of their members. They are still sore from the beating they took vicariously through Sceva's sons and Alexander in the theater. This whole ordeal was motivated by pure, unadulterated revenge. It was an illegal and unwise outburst that nearly brought bloodshed to our city and certainly is one more strike against our people in the eyes of Rome.

These troublemakers stirred up the temple shouting, "Men of Israel, help us! This is the man who teaches all men everywhere against our people and our law and this place. And besides, he has brought Greeks into the temple area and defiled this holy place." As you can imagine (I know many of you were there), people rushed from all directions. They grabbed Paul and dragged him outside the temple gate, locked it behind them, and beat him ruthlessly. While they were trying to assassinate him, the commander noticed the commotion and released his troops from the tower of Antonia. Roman guards with drawn swords streamed down the two stair cases, flooding the outer court. This alone stopped the mob, and just in the nick of time.

Paul was chained hand and foot. It was so unfair! It was the *mob* that deserved to be arrested. When Claudius asked them what Paul had done he got an earful. But none of it made sense. Their stories didn't match and they had no bonafide legal accusation. (Now where have we heard *that* before?!) At Claudius' command, the soldiers carried Paul back into the barracks. They actually had to hoist him up the stairs because of the volatile violence of the mob. The whole way they were shouting "Away with him!" It was an unruly and ungodly incident.

Now I have heard what some of you have said concerning Paul: "We don't want a criminal representing our church!" Need I remind you that my half-brother, the founder of this church and the Lord of all creation, was a crucified "criminal" under the hand of Rome?! Who among us looks more like Jesus than Paul? Don't despise his sufferings. To share in Christ's sufferings is a great honor. Rejoice when you encounter various trials because the testing of your faith produces endurance.

From now on, let no one cause trouble for Paul. Moreover, if you hear a brother spreading such lies, correct and rebuke him. Remember this: Whoever turns a sinner from the error of his way will save him from death and cover a multitude of sins.

My Witnesses

July 12, A.D. 57

Dear Cornelius,

I remember when I first got out of basic training and was placed under your command in Caesarea. You had recently become a Christian and kept talking about this Jew named Simon Peter who was an Apostle of Jesus of Nazareth. I never had the nerve to tell you what a fool I thought you were, but I'm sure you could read the disdain written in the lines of my face. As a Roman military leader I would follow you to the ends of the earth. Your religious commitment, however, I thought was insane. Why would anyone follow a crucified loser, a Jew, nonetheless, who had never been married, educated, published, or elected to a public office? What could such a religion amount to that promoted weakness – humbling yourself, praying for your enemies, seeking low positions at banquets? It just mystified me, that is, until last week.

I met Peter's counterpart, Paul. He also is an Apostle of Jesus and a leader among the Nazarenes. He got himself into trouble in the temple (which is not hard to do, you know). A riot broke out and Claudius ordered us to squelch it, which we were pleased to do I might add. By the time we got to Paul they had already dragged him outside the temple, locked the gate and beat him almost unconscious. I'm telling you, he was a mess.

We slapped chains on his hands and feet, not so much because he was a public threat, but to say to the crowd, "You can settle down. We'll see that justice is served." When Claudius asked the crowd what the problem was, mayhem broke loose. Some shouted one thing, others another. Since he was getting nowhere with his investigation, Claudius ordered Paul to be taken away. With a sweep of his hand he told us, "Get him out of here." Half-way up the steps, however, Paul asked, in Greek, "May I say something to you?" Whoa! We didn't know this guy was civilized. Lysias had just assumed he was that Egyptian revolutionary who led four thousand Jewish terrorists into the desert. Many of them were executed by Rome's superior military forces. We thought this beating was simply revenge for a failed liberation attempt. Paul answered, "An Egyptian?! No I'm a Jew from the noble city of Tarsus in Cilicia. I would like an opportunity to address my countrymen. I believe I can iron this whole thing out." Claudius responded, "What do I have to lose? Go ahead, give it your best shot!"

I didn't catch everything he said since he spoke in Aramaic. I had to eavesdrop on a Jewish translator. The bits and pieces I did catch, however, fascinated me. In fact, it's beginning to turn my life upside down. That's why I'm writing – to get your opinion on what Paul said.

Apparently this guy is well bred. He was born in that great university town of Tarsus and trained under some prominent Rabbi here in Jerusalem. I think his name is Gamaliel. Paul claims that he was a true-blue Jew, zealous for Yahweh and the law of Moses. And get this, he apparently used to imprison and kill Christians until he became one! Now, what do you suppose would turn a guy like that around 180 degrees? I mean, you don't normally see a persecutor become a preacher overnight!

Paul claimed he was converted by a vision on route to Damascus. He was going to extradite some of these Nazarenes back to Jerusalem to stand trial. It was about noon when he saw a bright light that dropped him to the ground. Then he heard a voice saying, "Saul! Saul! Why do you persecute me?" When he asked who it was, the voice said, "I am Jesus of Nazareth, whom you are persecuting." When it was all over, Paul was blind, and his companions had no idea what just happened. They had to lead him by the hand into the city. Three days later a Christian Jew named Ananias healed him, baptized him, and told him he would be a spokesman for God. To make a long story short, Paul eventually found himself back in Jerusalem. He was worshiping in the temple when he had another vision. This time Jesus said (so Paul claims), "Quick! Leave Jerusalem immediately, because they will not accept your testimony about me." Paul tried to argue with him but he lost. Paul quoted what Jesus supposedly said, "Go; I will send you far away to the Gentiles."

When the crowd heard the word "Gentiles" they went into a frenzy. They began throwing dust into the air and shouting, "Rid the earth of him! He's not fit to live!" I remember thinking to myself, "What's so bad about Gentiles?! I am one!"

These Jews said they wanted to execute Paul because he violated their temple. I don't think so. From their reaction to the word "Gentile," I'm convinced that they wanted to kill him because he liked people like me. Suddenly I was very curious about this Jew. He was the first one I had ever met who was so open to my friendship.

Claudius ordered us to carry him into the barracks. He was dead set on finding out what this man had done to foster such aggression. So at his command I strapped him up with leather thongs. I hated to do it, but I was a soldier under orders. I knew what was coming next. Paul was going to get the beating of his life. As I took off his tunic, I gasped at the scars. This was obviously not the first time he had been beaten. Paul knew what was coming too. He asked calmly, "Is it legal for you to flog a Roman citizen who hasn't even been found guilty?" What?! This guy was a Roman citizen. Man, I could get in big trouble just for tying him up. I ran to Lysias and said, "What do you think you're doing? This guy is a Roman citizen!" Claudius was as shocked as I was. He ran in and asked Paul, "Are you really a Roman citizen?" "Yes," Paul replied. Claudius, who had purchased his citizenship with big bucks asked Paul how he had gained his. Perhaps he, like Lysias was a "second-class" citizen. No way! Paul was born a Roman with all its inalienable rights. We had no choice but to let him go.

Had Paul wanted to, he could have reported us and caused all kinds of trouble for Claudius. He could have had us tied up and publically humiliated. Fortunately he didn't retaliate. That was the thing that got me thinking there was something different about him. Cornelius, please help me understand what makes this guy tick. What is it about these Christians that make them think and act so differently? How can they be such rebels without being rebellious? How can they live so counter to our culture without being revolutionaries? I am strangely attracted to this faith that lives in the world but is not of the world.

Sincerely Searching,

Andronicus

My Witnesses

From: Nicodemus II
To: James the Elder
RE: Paul and the Sanhedrin

As you know, Paul stood trial yesterday before the Sanhedrin. Claudius Lysias ordered this meeting in order to ascertain the charges against Paul. The fact is, we have no charges against him. He was arrested because some opportunists from Asia played off the religious fervor of the crowd in the temple. They used the people's zeal for God as a tool for personal revenge.

When Paul was brought before us, he opened the proceedings by claiming to have lived his outward piety without fault up to this very day. That was not exactly the best way to win friends in the Sanhedrin. They naturally took Paul's comments as a pugnacious rebuke of the high council. After all, if he was arrested by them he must certainly be guilty of *something*. Ananias, the high priest, ordered Paul to be slapped. You are aware, of course, that this is not legal.

Paul struck back, verbally that is. He said, "God will strike you, you whitewashed wall! You sit there to judge me according to the law, yet you yourself violate the law by commanding that I be struck!" We all gasped, both at Paul's brazen rebuke and his clarion assessment of Ananias' action. It didn't take long for this session to turn ugly.

Those standing near Paul rebuked him. "How dare you insult God's high priest!" Paul replied, "Brothers, I did not realize that he was the high priest; for it is written: 'Do not speak evil about the ruler of your people.'" On the surface, it appeared to be a genuine apology. Indeed, the council was in disorder since Claudius ordered us to assemble in such a rush. Ananias was not in his normal seating position nor was he dressed in the High Priestly garments. Furthermore, due to Paul's travels, it was very possible that he did not, in fact, realize Ananias had assumed the high office. On the other hand, there was something in Paul's voice. It was ever so subtle. There was something in the way he held his head that said, "I'm not completely serious." Within his apology was yet another rebuke that said, "A high priest ought not to act this way." I'm certain that I'm not the only one who caught it. The council erupted. Each man was discussing with his neighbor the actions of Paul and Ananias.

While we were in animated debate, Paul shouted over the top of us, "My brothers, I am a Pharisee, the son of a Pharisee. I stand on trial because of my hope in the resurrection of the dead." Talk about dividing your audience. That was a hot button among our council. Half the council, those who are Sadducees, was now convinced that Paul was a heretic and deserved to die. They don't believe in the resurrection of human souls either in the form of angels or other kinds of spirits. The other half, we Pharisees, suddenly thought this guy wasn't all that bad. We agreed with Paul about Ananias' corruption. We also now agreed with him about the resurrection from the dead.

It might appear that Paul was merely dividing the troops with an irrelevant issue. My perception is that Paul was right on target. We had no charge against him, not even concerning the temple. Trophimus' absence is proof enough of that. So why was he hated so? Because he was a follower of Jesus. And why was he a follower of Jesus? Because he has become convinced that Jesus rose from the dead. I must tell you, the evidence is compelling. So Paul was right when he said this trial was about belief in the resurrection. Furthermore, it was obvious that Paul was not going to get a fair hearing. So his comment was not only accurate, it was shrewd.

An argument broke out. Then came the tug of war . . . with Paul! The Pharisees were shouting, "We find nothing wrong with this man! Perhaps a spirit or an angel did speak to him." The Sadducees thought that was ridiculous and offensive, and told us so in no uncertain terms. Our argument was quickly escalating to a full-scale brawl. Once again the Roman soldiers intervened to save Paul's life. They ripped him from our hands before we ripped him apart. They whisked him away back into the barracks.

My Witnesses

I went secretly to see him this morning. He wanted me to relay this message to you. Last night he had a vision. The Lord stood near Paul and said, "Take courage! As you have testified about me in Jerusalem, so you must also testify in Rome." I don't know what that means, but I do know that Paul is in grave danger. I am writing to you to let you know what happened yesterday in our proceedings so you might be able to prepare a better legal defense for Paul. I wish you the best. Just as my father was a secret admirer of Jesus, so too I am of Christianity. I know that some of you would like for me to come out and affirm my faith publically. Perhaps someday, but now is not the time. There is much work to be done here on the "inside" of the Sanhedrin. You don't know how badly you need the allies you have here on the hill.

Until I do make my commitments public, I must ask you to keep this information in the strictest of confidence. Should you speak openly about this letter, it would certainly endanger my life and likely several others who are also allies here in the high council. Be wise and be patient. May the sovereign will of God prevail.

Classified: Top Secret

From: Joseph of Arimathea
To: James, the Elder
RE: URGENT: A Plot Against Paul's Life

Paul's life is in critical danger. This morning a group of forty militant fundamentalist extremists vowed together not to eat or drink until they have assassinated Paul. They went to the chief priests and elders, informing them of their commitment. They made arrangements to call an emergency meeting of the Sanhedrin tomorrow morning. They are going to go to the commander and ask that Paul be brought to them on the pretext of getting more accurate information about the case. If the commander agrees to this, Paul will be attacked somewhere between the tower of Antonia and the Hall of Gazith, where the meeting is to be held.

We have informed Paul's nephew of the plot. He has gone to tell Paul about it. That was the safest way for us to leak the information to Claudius. After all, the lad could go to Paul without any suspicion. None of us, however, could get close to Lysias without blowing our cover. According to our sources, the boy did go tell Paul and was then ushered by a centurion to Lysias, himself. The boy was then sent back home with strict orders not to talk to anyone about what was going to take place. Therefore, we don't know what Lysias said to him.

We don't think Claudius can afford a face to face stand-off with the Sanhedrin. He will not blatantly deny their request, openly accusing them of the plot. If he does do that, however, several of us, suspected of espionage, will be leaving Jerusalem on pretty short notice. We were fearful that Lysias was going to grant their request for a hearing, knowing that Paul would be assassinated. It would have cost him a few Roman soldiers. Yet he would come out looking like a hero, killing forty guerillas. However, about an hour ago (9 p.m.), our informant said there was a great deal of movement around the Tower.

My Witnesses

After people started bedding down for the night, closing their windows and putting out their oil lamps, Lysias mobilized his troops. Our source counted some 200 foot soldiers, another 200 spearmen and a retinue of 70 horses. The governor is apparently taking this thing seriously and moving Paul to a more secure location. We have no idea where, however.

We urge you to be up and ready early in the morning. Should you hear that Paul is being transferred to a meeting with the Sanhedrin, station your people all along the route. Have them keep their eyes peeled for daggers or archers. You must blow any cover these potential assassins have. Please be aware, however, that Lysias likely knows the attempt is to be made, so it is the soldiers you will be warning, not him.

Do not go to Lysias, since we have already done that. Should you go as well you will endanger our covert operation here on the hill. If he does not respond to the warning we have already given him that will mean that he is a friend of the Sadducees and your involvement will endanger our lives. Furthermore, James, do not try to contact me and do not speak of this letter to anyone. I am being watched like a hawk. My love for your brother was evident at his burial. Any contact you make with me will likely result in my excommunication and/or execution. I am at risk for even sending this letter. I urge you to destroy it immediately.

We pray that Yahweh may rescue our kinsman Paul from the hands of his enemies, our own countrymen.

February 10, A.D. 58

Dear Dr. Luke,

I have some information for you that I thought you might find interesting. My father, Philip the Evangelist, is good friends with Cornelius, the retired centurion. He has some inside sources in Felix's cabinet. He learned the following information from the court reporter and passed it on to me and my father at a banquet last night.

You remember how we begged Paul not to go up to Jerusalem. It was only a week later that I was out in the garden early one morning. I heard a parade coming into town. There must have been 70 horsemen. It was so unusual that I went and called my father. Well, here they came. We couldn't believe what we saw. We squinted and rubbed our eyes. Sure enough, it was Paul . . . in chains. What had he gotten himself into this time?

Cornelius went to work immediately trying to find out what was going on and how he could help. Five days later here came the delegation from Jerusalem. Ananias the High Priest was at the helm of a group of Elders. They had hired some slick lawyer named Tertullus to bring charges against Paul. When they brought him before the Governor, Tertullus went to work buttering him up. "Oh Felix, we have had such peace under your superior leadership. Your foresight has brought about reforms in this nation. Everywhere and in every way, most excellent Felix, we acknowledge this with profound gratitude." Give me a break! Felix is an egotistical, antisemitic, crooked politician. He murdered one of our High Priests and has corrupted our government.

Tertullus went on to accuse Paul of being a troublemaker, stirring up riots among the Jews all over the world, being the ringleader of the Nazarenes and desecrating the temple. Each of these charges were straw men. Paul was just raring to go. I mean, this was just too easy. They should have been out of court by noon!

My Witnesses

When the governor motioned for Paul to speak, he didn't kiss up to the guy. He simply said, "I know that for a number of years you have been a judge over this nation; so I gladly make my defense." It was polite yet true. Felix had been in the area long enough to be well acquainted with Jewish culture and thought. That should have been to Paul's advantage.

He tackled the accusations systematically. *#1 Being a troublemaker and stirring up riots:* False. Paul has only been in the area for twelve days. That's really not enough time to stir up trouble (it took the locals to do that). During those days he pretty much minded his own business. When he was in the temple, he wasn't arguing theology or politics, he was worshiping God. In fact, he didn't carry on debates in the synagogue, in the market-place or anywhere else.

#2 Desecrating the temple: False. They have no evidence (i.e. no carcass of Trophimus).

#3 He is a ringleader of the Nazarenes: True, True, True. However, this is not a new and illicit sect. This is the hope of our forefathers, predicted by the prophets. Paul said, "I am faithful to the Scriptures, both the Law and the Prophets. I share the hope of my countrymen in the resurrection from the dead." At this point Paul started preaching. He just can't help himself sometimes.

Paul went on to say, "Felix, you want to know what a rotten guy I am? Why I came to Jerusalem with a sacks of cash as an offering for the poor of my people! Then, oh my goodness, I went to the temple to complete a vow. It was there that they found me minding my own business and ceremonially clean." I think Felix got the point. Paul wasn't done yet, though. He brought up a very important legal point. Who was it that accused Paul of desecrating the temple? Why, it was a group of rabble rousers from Asia. Where are they now? Back in Asia! You can't condemn a man when his accusers won't even step forward! It's only been a week since his arrest. Surely they could have stayed another week if there were any real charges against him. Paul said, "The only thing I've done remotely wrong is shouting out in the Sanhedrin,

'It is concerning the resurrection of the dead that I am on trial before you today.'" I doubt it was an apology. Rather, I think Paul was preaching again. Felix understood that too. That's why he cut him off saying, "When Lysias the commander comes I will decide your case." That was stupid! Lysias was not necessary to decide these proceedings. Besides, Lysias already sent a letter with Paul explaining what had happened. In the letter he said, and I quote, "I found that the accusation had to do with questions about their law, *but there was no charge against him that deserved death or imprisonment* [italics added]."

Felix should have let Paul go. But he kept him in protective custody for two reasons. First, he was hoping to get a bribe from Paul, especially after he learned that Paul had collected a considerable sum from the churches of Macedonia, Achaia and Asia. Second, he was interested in Paul's preaching.

Paul was right. Felix is well acquainted with Judaism. He is also quite familiar with Christianity. He learned about The Way from several sources. He, of course, has his informants who keep their fingers on the pulse of cultural and political movements in Palestine. He also has a number of his own cabinet that are converts to Christ. (Cornelius' effect is still felt in the governmental circles of Caesarea.) His most "active" source, however, was his own wife, Drusilla. She is a wretch of a woman. It was her father who killed the Apostle James and was consequently executed by God. I think she is still bitter about that. It was her uncle who killed John the Baptist and held Jesus on trial. It was her Grandfather who tried to murder the infant Jesus with the slaughter of the Bethlehem infants. Yeah, I'd say she knows a bit about the Jesus movement!

Felix and Drusilla sometimes go listen to Paul preach. He doesn't pull any punches. The usual topics under the banner of "faith in Christ" are: Righteousness, self-control and judgment to come. Felix knows little about any of these. He usually winds up cutting Paul off before he can start singing "I Surrender All." He'll say something like, "O my, look at the time. I gotta go.

My Witnesses

Listen, when I get a chance I'll come back at a more convenient time and we can finish this discussion."

Luke, rally the troops to pray for Paul. I don't know how he is going to fare under Felix. As it stands, it is a cat and mouse game – Felix is just toying with him. If God doesn't intervene, we may see one of the world's greatest preachers wither in protective custody.

Love,

Huldah

P.S. My father told me about your research on the early events of Christianity. I do pray that is going well for you. While you're stuck here in Palestine it would be a good time to speak to the early eyewitnesses. If you need someone to proof your manuscript I would be glad to help.

Trial Record # 251-12

Recorder: Philologus
Date: September 8, A.D. 59

Background: After Felix had been exiled by Nero because of the complaints of the Jews, Porcius Festus succeeded him as governor. Three days after arriving in the province he took a trip to Jerusalem to give ear to his Jewish constituents. The chief priests and Elders appeared before him, still fulminating against Paul of Tarsus. They requested that Paul be extradited back to Jerusalem for trial. Festus refused, fearing an ambush along the way. (Further investigation confirmed his fears). Nearly a week and a half later, both parties arrived back in Caesarea. The following morning court was convened.

The Jews: They brought many serious charges against Paul. They have been stricken from the court's record, however, because none of them could be substantiated.

Paul: He categorically denied any wrong-doing against the Jewish law, the temple or Caesar. His defense was "short and sweet."

Festus: He invited Paul to wave his rights as a Roman citizen and return to Jerusalem to stand trial before his own council with Festus as the moderator. Festus correctly perceived that this was what the Jews wanted. Paul correctly perceived that this was certain suicide. So he declined Festus' offer. Rather, in a surprise and very risky legal maneuver, he appealed to Caesar, namely Nero, the despot of the Empire. Festus was forced to confer with his legal advisors to discuss what kind of options were open to them. Essentially he had no options. Once the prisoner appealed to Caesar the court case was closed and Festus' only further obligation was to send him to Rome with a letter of explanation as to the charges brought against him and the reasons why it could not be equitably settled in a lower court. This presented a problem to Festus because there were no valid charges and hence no reason to hold Paul as a prisoner. Nonetheless, because of the political pressure of the Jewish leaders, he could not afford to let this prisoner go, at the risk of social unrest and rioting. He could not admit this, however, for such a confession would be tantamount to admitting failure as a Roman ruler and prematurely end his career. Festus and his advisors are now attempting to draft a letter that will adequately explain their quandary to the Emperor.

Dear Luke,

In response to your request for information about Herod and Bernice, I could tell you more than you ever wanted to know, believe me. I grew up with their great uncle, Herod Antipas, the Tetrarch of Galilee and Perea. It's a fact I'm not proud of, but this childhood friend of mind murdered John the Baptist and tried our precious Lord, Jesus Christ. I am well acquainted with the whole family and their antics. Some of my own relatives, who are still intimately connected with the "king of the Jews," have informed me about Herod's interview with Paul.

About two weeks after Festus took office, Herod went down to Caesarea to congratulate him. I think it was one part professional courtesy and two parts excuse for a party. He brought Bernice with him. She is his sister and by some accounts also his lover. My acquaintance with the Herod family leads me to believe these reports are probably true.

Festus took this opportunity to discuss Paul's case with Herod since he and Bernice were making an extended visit. He explained how Paul was a political prisoner left over from the reign of Felix. He also described how eager the Jews were to have him executed. He was not charged with social crimes but religious offenses. This threw Festus for a loop. He didn't know how to settle such disputes and asked if Herod would listen to Paul and give his opinion about what to write to Nero since Paul had appealed to the Emperor.

King Herod seemed delighted at the opportunity. After all, it was his own father who had murdered James, the Apostle, and was shortly thereafter eaten by worms. Herod had a personal interest in this Jesus movement. They scheduled the big bash for the following day. All kinds of dignitaries were there all dressed up like it was a ball. There were robes and crowns, escorts and *hors d'oeuvres*. Everybody who was anybody was there: military leaders, politicians, businessmen, you name it.

Into the middle of all this pomp and circumstance walks Paul, the prisoner. He was dressed in a simple Palestinian tunic draped with chains. You know, Paul is not an impressive physical specimen. There he stood, a short, bald Jew in his late 50's. It seemed strange that such a beleaguered figure could creat such a stir. In fact, I wonder, when the history books are written, how many will remember Paul and how many will remember Festus and his friends. All those "dignitaries" would probably feel scandalized if they could see into the future and realize just how unimportant they are in light of this one lone man – God's chosen instrument of the Gospel.

Herod gave Paul permission to speak. He opened by saying, "King Agrippa, I'm delighted to have the opportunity to tell you my side of the story, especially since you are so well acquainted with our people and our customs. Please listen to me patiently. This could take a while." Now that Paul finally had someone who could understand the issues at stake, his defense suddenly became long and intricate. Before he just categorically denied any wrongdoing.

Paul told about his conversion. He used to be the strictest kind of Pharisee, a persecutor of the church (which Paul described in vivid detail). However, when the Lord Jesus appeared to him on the road to Damascus, he realized that he had risen from the dead. That changed everything in an instant. If Jesus is raised, then man's greatest enemy, "Death," has been defeated. If Jesus is raised then he truly is the Son of God. If Jesus is raised, then we must listen to his words and follow his ways. If Jesus is raised then his work on the cross really did take away our sins. This does, indeed, change everything! (I understand Paul got pretty animated at this point.)

To make a very long story short, Paul explained how Jesus commissioned him to preach the gospel to the Gentiles. He told them that their sins were forgiven and they could be sanctified by faith. Come to think of it, Paul wasn't doing too bad a job preaching to Herod and Festus at that very moment. He recounted his ministry and how many Gentiles became believers. "That, King Agrippa," said Paul, "is why my countrymen had me arrested." Herod himself was well aware of the Jewish prejudice against Gentiles. He had often borne the brunt of it.

At this point Paul kicked it into high gear. He knew that Herod was familiar with the Jewish Scriptures. So Paul did what Paul does best. He started going through the O.T. passage by passage showing that the Messiah must suffer and die and become a light to the Gentiles. Paul was like a freight train getting up a full head of steam, driving home the point that Jesus is the Messiah of God. He began to take aim at his target and press for a decision.

Festus saw where he was going. With an untimely and ill-mannered outburst he stopped Paul. He shouted, "You are out of your mind, Paul! You've read one too many books and it's driven you insane." Paul, however, responded with controlled force: "I am not insane, most excellent Festus. What I am saying is true and reasonable. The king is familiar with these things, and I can speak freely to him. I am convinced that none of this has escaped his notice, because it was not done in a corner." Then looking straight into Agrippa's soul he said, "King Agrippa, do you believe the prophets? I know you do . . ."

Agrippa was in a serious dilemma. If he disagreed with Paul, he would be both illogical and impious. After all, the Scriptures point unmistakably to Jesus. Yet if he agreed with Paul, that would call for a decision. He was not willing to humble himself, especially in front of his colleagues. Nor was he willing to change his lifestyle. Like most religious politicians, he had enough religion to make him uncomfortable, but not enough to actually change him.

So Agrippa replied, "Do you think that you can convert me with such a little bit . . ." What? A little bit of time? A paucity of evidence? What was he talking about? Was he being serious or cynical? Was he saying Paul might convert him with a bit more time or with better evidence? My suspicion is that Herod was purposefully enigmatic. It made him sound intelligent when in reality, he was just copping out of making a decision.

Paul wasn't about to let it go, however. He pressed him, "With a little bit or much – I pray to God that not only you but all who are listening to me today may become what I am . . . except for these chains." Paul had a strange smirk on his face.

Paul was ready to press on further but the king rose from his chair. The governor and Bernice followed. The party was then over, of course, and everybody left. Once they got out of the room, Herod said, "This man is not doing anything that deserves death or imprisonment." It didn't take a genius to figure that one out! That's what Claudius Lysias had concluded. That's what Felix said. That's what Festus decided. And now, King Agrippa conferred. Every single Roman leader that heard Paul came to the same conclusion: Paul is innocent of these charges. Agrippa said to Festus, "This man could have been set free if he had not appealed to Caesar." Set free my foot! That was not going to happen in a million years. It almost makes one believe that it is the hand of God rather than the chains of men that are keeping Paul in prison. I don't understand why God is not releasing him and frankly I don't much appreciate it. Nevertheless, perhaps God's ways are higher than our ways. Perhaps he can work all things together for good for those who love him.

In Christ,

Manaen

A Travel Report by Julius to His Excellency

We set sail for Italy on September 11th, A.D. 59. I, Julius, boarded a ship from Adramyttium. It was returning to its home port, so we decided to go as far as the western coast of Asia Minor on this vessel. We loaded several prisoners on board, including Paul and his two servants, Aristarchus and Luke, the physician.

We made good time on this first leg of the trip and landed in Sidon the second day. Paul had friends there he wanted to see. He seemed like a nice enough fellow and a man of some stature. He was a Roman citizen who had not been charged with any serious crime. I therefore saw no harm in letting him go ashore so that his friends could supply his needs. Besides, it's never hurt a ship to have a wealthy man on board.

On this second leg of the trip the winds were against us. In fact, we had to pass under the shelter of Cyprus in order to make any headway. Once we passed Cyprus, we then had to go across the open sea toward Cilicia and Pamphylia. Finally we landed at Myra in Lycia. There we changed ships. We boarded a cargo vessel from Alexandria in Egypt. It was a large ship, packed with wheat, heading to Rome.

This third leg of the trip was tedious. We crept along the coast. After many days we finally arrived at Cnidus. We could go no further west due to the winds. We then decided to head southwest and sail under the shelter of Crete opposite Salmone. Again we crept along the coast until we arrived at a harbor called "Fair Havens." The little town of Lasea was a couple hours away, but it was far too small to host the 276 men on board. Sailors do like their wine, women and song, you know. We discussed it with the crew. Should we stick it out here for the winter or try to make it over to Phoenix? That was a harbor around the next bend about 36 miles away. The ship would be better protected there from the winter storms and there was a large town nearby. If we could safely sail for three or four more hours we could be there. I know that sounds like a short distance, but it was already late October, when sailing on the Mediterranean is dangerous. Paul objected strenuously to the move. He said, "Men, I can see that our voyage is going to be disastrous and bring great loss to ship and cargo, and to our own lives also." What a pessimist! Both the owner of the ship and the captain he had hired to sail the vessel agreed to go on. In fact, most of the sailors agreed that they could make it. I had the authority, as a centurion, to keep them there or send them on. Now that I look back, I saw that I should have taken Paul's advice. But how could I have known that then? It was one rabbi against the majority of the sailors, the owner and the captain. We pressed on.

We waited for the right time. Soon a gentle south wind began to blow. We thanked the gods for our good fate and weighed anchor. As soon as we rounded the bend and were exposed to the open sea, the heavens broke loose. A hurricane force wind from the Northeast swept over Mount Ida and came crashing against the sea. It hit us broadside and threatened to tear our boat apart. We had no choice but to give way and let it drive us out to sea.

About twenty-three miles west of Crete is a small island named Cauda. As we passed under its shelter we made emergency preparations to ride out the storm. First, we pulled in the lifeboat. It was half filled with water so we wore some wicked blisters on our hands getting it on board. Next we tied up the boat with ropes to reinforce it as best we could. Then we lowered the sea anchor to slow us down. We were afraid of being driven south into the sand bars of North Africa, the ones they call "Syrtis."

Man did we ever take a beating! In fact, the next day, as we continued to take on water, we decided to cast overboard all non-essentials. Poor Paul was fit to be tied when we threw out his scrolls. After the third day we were still too heavy so the sailors threw out all the rigging. That meant we could no longer sail the ship. All we could do was hope to beach it somewhere.

After a week and a half of this the men were fatigued and losing all hope of being saved. Paul stood and addressed the beleaguered sailors, "Men, you should have taken my advice not to sail from Crete." Had it been a mere "I told you so," Paul probably would have been the next thing thrown overboard. But he was not being vindictive. He was simply trying to get us to listen to him this time a little better than we had the last time. He went on: "I urge you to keep up your courage, because not one of you will be lost; only the ship will be destroyed." Hello! Paul, we are in the middle of the ocean! How on earth can you say the ship will be lost but none of us will drown? His answer was absurd. He said, "Last night an angel of the God whose I am and whom I serve stood beside me and said, 'Do not be afraid, Paul, You must stand trial before Caesar; and God has graciously given you the lives of all who sail with you.' So keep up your courage, men, for I have faith in God that it will happen just as he told me. Nevertheless, we must run aground on some Island." We thought the guy was delusional. We were glad his faith sustained him. But for those of us who live in the real world, such naivety was no great comfort.

Two weeks had passed and we were still being driven across the Adriatic Sea. We had seen neither sun nor stars so we had no idea where we were. About midnight, the sailors on watch heard some breakers. By this they knew we were near land. They measured to see how deep the water was – 120 feet. Just a little while later, they measured again and it was 90 feet. That meant we were quickly approaching land but it was too dark to see anything. We were glad for the land, but terrified about being dashed against the rocks. We let down four anchors from the back of the boat and prayed that they would hold us until daylight.

Several of the sailors got into the lifeboat and were about to escape. Paul blew the whistle on them. He told me, "Look, God promised that because of me all of you will be saved. However, if you let these guys leave on the lifeboat, all bets are off." I ordered a couple of soldiers to cut the ropes holding the boat. It fell quickly to the water and drifted off into the night. The soldiers were livid. "What did you do that for you *&%#@ idiot!" They claimed they were only going to lay anchors from the front of the boat. Fat chance! The sailors shouted at the soldiers calling them ignorant landlubbers. The soldiers shouted back, calling them undisciplined, disloyal cowards. When they put their hands on their swords we knew things were getting out of hand. I had to intervene to calm everyone down.

Paul also helped. Just before dawn he urged them to eat something. He told them they would need their energy to survive. He lifted up the bread to heaven and prayed a Jewish blessing on it. Everyone felt better after they had eaten. We took the leftovers and threw it overboard.

At daylight we spotted a sandy beach. The captain hoisted the foresail and lowered the rudders. We were going to try to beach the craft. Unfortunately the front of the boat hit an underwater sandbar and stuck fast. The waves continued to pummel us from behind. It didn't take long for the badly bruised ship to break apart.

The soldiers made plans to execute the prisoners rather than let them escape and risk incurring their punishment. I, however, prevented them. I like Paul and would hate to lose such a valuable advisor. I convinced the soldiers to swim to shore first. Those that couldn't swim were to float on pieces of the ship. Then we would release the prisoners and they could be safely rounded up as they arrived on shore. It took a little while, but every last person made it safely.

We found out later that the Island was Malta. The people were exceptionally hospitable. After wintering there we found another Alexandrian ship which gave us safe passage to Puteoli. Thus we reached Rome. That, your Excellency, is how we lost our ship but not a single prisoner.

I realize that Paul is to stand trial before the Emperor. Let it be known that whatever crimes he may be accused of, I found him to be a great personal help and a man of wisdom. After observing him these past four months I am convinced that he is a dynamic and charismatic leader but poses no threat to the security of the Empire. For what it's worth, I took a great risk to spare his life and I would pray that my example would set a precedent for his future trial.

February 14, A.D. 60

From: Publius, Governor of Malta
RE: A Character reference for Paul of Tarsus

To whom it may concern:

I understand that Paul of Tarsus is to stand trial before the Emperor due to some unsubstantiated charges by his countrymen. It is my hope that this character reference will help persuade his Majesty that this man, Paul, is a Roman citizen of honorable standing and a benefit to whatever community in which he finds himself.

I'm sure that Julius has informed you about the sunken Alexandrian wheat vessel. It was late October of last year and our little Island had been pummeled by a storm for more than two weeks. It was rainy and cold so nobody went out of doors except for necessities. One morning, however, our shepherd boy raised quite a ruckus. He was the first to spot the ship in the bay. We weren't used to seeing ships on our side of the Island. They always anchored in the port on the other side. There is a good reason for that. While our beach has beautiful sand, it also has an underwater sandbar that is treacherous.

It didn't take long for the whole village to assemble at the beach. They tried to shout at the captain of the ship to turn around. But it was no good. They plowed right into the sandbar. We stoked up fires as best we could with wet kindling and tried to greet the sailors with blankets the moment they made it to shore. Amazingly, every last person made it safely. It was a day to rejoice.

Our joy was tempered, however, when we learned that there were a number of criminals among the sailors. We're a small rural town, unaccustomed to felons. We got really nervous, especially after what happened to Paul. You see, he threw a bunch of brush onto the fire and got bit by a viper. Apparently the flames stirred the serpent which then latched onto Paul's arm. He shook it off into the fire. We held our breaths and watched. We were convinced that the gods were involved. While Paul escaped his fate of drowning, the goddess Justice was not going to let him off the hook. Indeed, Deity was involved in the incident, but not like we assumed. When Paul did not swell up and die, it got people's attention, believe you me! We were all poised to listen.

I welcomed him and his two companions into my home. I was delighted to have Luke since he was a physician. My father was sick in bed with recurring fevers and dysentery. That's pretty tough on an old man. We were afraid that we were going to lose him. Luke checked him over. He too was pretty pessimistic. Paul, however, went in and prayed for him. Afterward he placed his hands on my father and healed him. No kidding, this was the most amazing thing I had ever seen in my life.

It didn't take long before the whole Island had heard about the miracle and brought their sick to my estate. Those that Luke couldn't help, Paul did. We are terribly indebted to these two. In fact, when they left, we sent them away with all kinds of supplies and gifts. After all, they deserved some kind of remuneration for their services.

They spent three months with us through the winter. As soon as they could leave we put them aboard another Alexandrian ship, the one with Castor and Pollux as the figure head. They should arrive in Rome via Syracuse, Rhegium and Puteoli. Please know that these men are beloved by our community and offered us an invaluable service. The Empire would be poorer if this man Paul were lost to her citizens.

A Letter to James and the Elders of Jerusalem

Aquila, a servant of Jesus Christ and companion of Paul in his Roman imprisonment, along with my wife Priscilla, as well as Luke, Epaenetus and the whole church of Rome. To the saints in Jerusalem. Grace to you and Peace from God our Father and the Lord Jesus Christ.

We always thank God for you when we pray because we know of your faith and repentance that opened up the Gospel to the entire Roman world. We are grateful for the support you gave to our brother Paul in his imprisonment there in Jerusalem as well as Caesarea. We are writing to let you know that our great God is continuing your work of compassion through our hands.

Paul arrived late this winter. When we heard that he was coming up from Melita through Rhegium and Puteoli, we sent a delegation to intercept their party. Some of the brothers went as far as the Forum of Appius. Others only traveled the thirty-three miles to Three Taverns. When Paul saw us his heart was encouraged. We all burst into tears as we embraced and heard his story of near death and miraculous rescue.

When he arrived in Rome he rented an apartment where he will stay until his trial. He has a round-the-clock visitors, of course, with the soldiers who guard him. He was only here three days when he invited the Jewish leaders to his place. He wanted them to know that he had no accusation against his people. But his real agenda was to evangelize them. It was a risky move. Considering that he was on trial for stirring up his people, and considering his track record with Jewish evangelism, Paul was taking a great risk inviting them over. But as you all know by now, when it comes to sharing his faith Paul just can't help himself. He is an gospel gladiator!

Paul explained what had happened in Jerusalem and why he was now in Rome. The Jews listened attentively. In fact, they were surprisingly open to hear him out. They had heard about Paul but had not received any recent or specific legal charges. They had also heard of Christianity. In fact, word on the street is that Christians are incestuous cannibals because of their communion service and brotherly affections. Moreover, they are charged with being antisocial atheists because they have abandoned Roman social life and the Greek Pantheon. These are serious charges, although twisted and false.

So they set a date when they could all sit down and discuss Christianity and its doctrines. When the day arrived, Paul's place was packed. There was standing room only when they began that morning, and nobody left all day long. They turned from passage to passage, discussing the Messiah and how Jesus fulfilled his role. As you could probably predict, the Jews were divided. Many were convinced that Jesus is the Messiah of God, and put their faith in him. Many others, however, refused to believe and receive life.

As the sun was setting and people were getting up to leave, Paul made one final statement. He said, "The Holy Spirit spoke the truth to your forefathers when he said through Isaiah the prophet: 'Go to this people and say, you will be ever hearing but never understanding; you will be ever seeing but never perceiving. For this people's heart has become calloused; they hardly hear with their ears, and they have closed their eyes. Otherwise they might see with their eyes, hear with their ears, understand with their hearts and turn, and I would heal them.'"

With this indictment Paul released himself of responsibility for their rejection. He shook out his cloak, in a manner of speaking. From that point, he turned to the Gentiles who eagerly accepted Jesus as Lord. It was a big day and a turning point in the direction of the Church of Rome, perhaps of the whole world.

Paul is in prison and his future is uncertain. But the gospel is free from all hindrance and liberating is for all who accept it. Even with Paul in chains, the Kingdom of God marches on victoriously. Rejoice with us in the victory of God here in Rome.

May the peace of God rule in your hearts and churches brothers, Amen.

A Prologue to the Acts of the Holy Spirit

The previous documents, letters and testimonials are my primary sources for this forthcoming volume. These are my witnesses from Jerusalem, Judea and Samaria, and around the Roman Empire. Through these eyewitnesses I have carefully reconstructed the events surrounding the Jesus movement. Through their eyes we can see the continuing incarnation of Jesus Christ in his bride. Here you will witness healings and persecutions, sermons and adventures, courts and synagogues, the power of the Holy Spirit and the opposition of demons. But most of all, you will watch as people give their lives to Jesus Christ: Foreigners, governors, women, slaves, magicians, Roman guards, Greek Areopagites, Ethiopian treasurers, Jewish priests, entire households at once. You name it, they came and bowed the knee to King Jesus, the one true *Pontificus Maximus*.

I have carefully traced the phenomenal rise of Christianity. Like a lily among weeds, The Way has grown up among pagans. It has blossomed, giving hope and life to those who knew only hopelessness and darkness. I confess, I am not an impartial reporter. I too have been swept up in the mighty current of this movement. I, Luke, a Gentile of no account, and outsider of God's Kingdom, have been grafted into the Olive tree of God's people.

I humbly offer this volume to squelch some rumors and to substantiate others. I only ask that you not read it dispassionately. It will not bear such treatment. For the things that have taken place among us are anything but mundane. So with a prayer for the Spirit's conviction on my readers, I offer you these, my witnesses.

Luke